THE

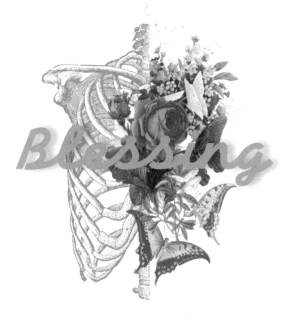

Blessing

Of Somatic Therapy Techniques:
A Comprehensive Beginner's Guide to Release Trauma, Reveal Peace, and Rewire Mind-Body Connections

By: Naty H.E.A.L.S.

Khalessi Publications LLC

This book is dedicated to:

My Wife, Natasha, for your love, patience, kindness, and partnership in life and in all I do. Thank you for being supportive and attentive.

My children, Demi, Saevonni, and Nalani, for inspiring me to start my healing journey. For being my daily inspiration to keep fighting for self-peace and good health.

To my Ama and Apa (my grandmother and grandfather),

Trinidad Jacobo y Jose Jacobo, for risking so much to give their family a better life. I am grateful for their love and their prayers.

Ama, for teaching me what the love of family was and how to hold onto the motherly strength she passed on to me.

Apa, for inspiring me to always keep praying and to always stay grateful.

My mother, Maria De Los Angeles Jacobo, for teaching me to persist against all odds and to always hold on to my faith.

My sister, Mariela Mondragon, for always believing in me and supporting my dreams. For teaching me to PUSH through the pain (Pray Until Something Happens).

To Memaw, Eldeen Davis, for always being a loving, supportive, *and kind ray of sunshine in my life.*

To my Creator, for leading my path toward the wisdom of natural healing, and for providing the benefits for my mind, body, and spirit.

Finally, to you, the reader, and all those seeking answers on how to create and maintain a healthier lifestyle.

You're not on your own; I'll be by your side as you tackle this.

Table of Contents

The Blessing

Natural healing with Somatic Therapy is a BLESSING.

It is the life-changing tool that I used to connect with my higher self, my healing self, after decades of self-hate, self-doubt, and feeling stuck in the same dysfunctional patterns.

It is through my somatic and complementary practices that I realized that I am whole.

I am genuine.

I am endless.

I am everlasting.

I am unlimited.

I am no longer consumed by misery and torment.

This is my authentic pure nature.

Naty

"The greatest weapon against stress is our ability to choose one thought over another."

– William James. 1842-1910

(William James Quotes. n.d.)

"Peace comes from within. Do not seek it without"

– Buddha 563 BC - 483 BC

(Buddha Quotes. n.d.)

Now is the time to relieve stress
and anxiety to reveal your authentic pure nature.
As you begin, I ask you to keep in mind one of my favorite sayings:
All healing starts with self-healing

Chapter 1:
Awakening Wisdom

What to expect in this chapter:

Introduction to Somatic Therapy
What to expect within the book
My story
Mind-Body, Resilience, Neuroplasticity
Building a strong mind-body connection
True self and authenticity
Self-limiting perspectives

Initium Novum (A New Beginning)

Within every heartbeat lies the untold story of your life's journey. Your body is connected in unseen ways. Within these lines, we shall uncover the mystery of natural healing using the narrative of your life experiences discovered through Somatic Therapy. It's truly fascinating how your body holds onto so much information.

Take a few moments to find a comfortable, quiet place to relax without interruption. Once you feel settled, close your eyes and focus on your breath. Inhale and silently count to three, then exhale on four. Repeat this process for three additional cycles while concentrating on your body. Take note of any sensations you feel – where are they located, what do they feel like, and so on. If you're experiencing discomfort or tension, try to release that energy with each subsequent breath. Remember, this is a moment to focus solely on your body and what it needs using your mind-body connection. By learning to decrypt this data with the methods discussed in this book, you'll be able to truly heal from the inside out. It's incredible what your body is capable of, and I feel so grateful to have the opportunity to explore this more profound level of healing with you. You may have picked up this book because of the stunning faces on the cover awakening your curiosity or because your current problems aren't allowing you to progress in life, and you're seeking help. I'm not referring to financial progress but rather emotional, mental, and spiritual disturbances that may hold you back.

I am passionate about this topic because a staggering 70% of each and every person on Earth has experienced a traumatic event, and 30% of those have experienced four or more (BioBeats, 2021).

I am part of the 30%.

This means that a staggering 550 million people worldwide and a heart-wrenching 230 million in the United States alone have endured the harrowing grasp of a traumatic event. Among them, 12 million bear the weight of PTSD. It's a painful reality that hundreds of millions endure the crushing weight of suffering each day simply because these vital coping mechanisms are just not taught where they call home. I'm devoted to this because many of my family members and loved ones have suffered a lifetime of trauma and stress. These techniques are often considered just an "alternative" medicine, which to some means less effective. Still, others believe certain techniques are "weird," voodoo, or only for hippies. But the truth is these techniques are the missing link to fully healing the entire body and mind.

> Did you know that trauma is the #1 risk factor for substance abuse and nearly all behavioral health issues? Did you know that depression stands out as the number one factor causing disability? (Spinhoven et al., 2014)

Yet, Western medicine is only recently discovering how trauma actually affects the body and how to treat it (Barratt, 2013). Somatic Therapy is irreplaceable and invaluable in regard to holistic healing, as traditional talk therapies alone are not sufficient to address deep-rooted issues and trauma.

After completing this book, should you find yourself pouring your heart out to your physician about your trauma and asking about Somatic Therapy or the innate healing potential within your body, don't be alarmed if you're met with a blank expression. I've seen it many times, and it's our sad reality that this crucial aspect of healing often remains outside the realm of conventional medical practice. It's not their fault; it's typically not part of the standard training. In my upbringing, going to the doctor was synonymous with popping a pill for a cold or headache and applying a cast for a fracture. Our medical system's most significant limitation is masking symptoms and ignoring root issues.

While our healthcare system has its benefits, it was designed to alleviate our symptoms to make us feel better in the short term rather than addressing the underlying causes. This affects all of us in one way or another. Everyone has loved ones who depend on this system for their care. Growing up on Medicaid, it was difficult to find medical professionals who would take the time to listen to me and not rush out of the door after prescribing a new medication. Or worse, some who didn't trust me when I tried to clarify what I was going through. In the Latino community, seeking therapy is often stigmatized as "para los locos" (for the crazy), and discussing family issues with others is frowned upon as "chisme" (gossip). Instead, prayer, fasting, and obedience was my expected solution. Yet, there was always something missing; the essence that I was not quite right was relentlessly present. The painful truth is that my trauma had never fully been treated; the surface wounds were just covered up. It was only when my therapist suggested that I try meditating that I stumbled upon the truth about my body and healing, the blessing of Somatic Therapy.

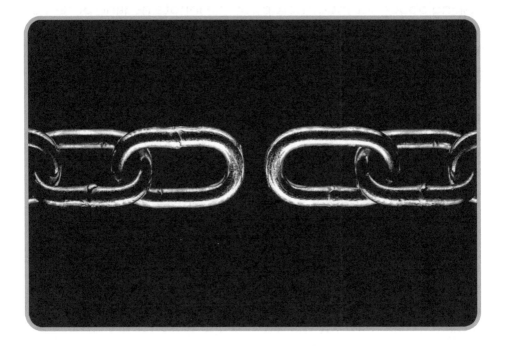

I finally learned what I needed to do to treat the root of the problem. At last, I located the very core of the issue: my mind-body connection was having significant issues. This was one of the missing links disregarded by all of my physicians and the conventional system of Western medicine.

They tend to be fixated on studying the mind but often neglect the role that the connection to the body plays. The issue was that my trauma was never fully treated; instead, the symptoms were being covered up. It wasn't until I learned about this missing link, that I could finally get to the core issue. I learned the truth about my body and healing. To be clear, healing with Somatic Therapy is not a new concept. Traditional medicine and ancient societies have effectively used natural healing techniques for thousands of years. Why are we not taught these proven and effective ways of naturally healing trauma and stress??! Well, that's for another time.

Have you ever heard someone say the phrase, "I just hate people!"?

When I hear someone say this phrase to me, it means they are annoyed by being around miserable people. Miserable people are usually stressed or traumatized people; and no one likes to be around that.

What if I prove to you that Somatic Therapy can literally make the world a happier, better place because it makes happier people? What if it could make the world less racist and less sexist?

It could be the most powerful tool in the world that everyone should seek, right?!

Somatic Therapy is vital to life because living on guard or under stress doesn't allow you to let love in, and love is life.

Your body is more than just a container or collection of cells that your mind controls. Explore the captivating study of Somatic Therapy, where your body plays a vital role in the restorative process. By accessing your physical sensations, memories, and emotions, you can liberate yourself from the burdens of stress and trauma. This book will explore treatments and practices designed to help soothe the damage of trauma and stress while restoring the mind-body connection.

Let's first ensure that we are on the same page regarding the meaning of trauma and stress. Trauma is the psychological and emotional negative consequence of intensely unsettling and painful experiences that overwhelm your coping ability. Trauma changes how you cope. This means you can no longer effectively deal with everyday life as you would have without the experience(s). It can disrupt your sense of internal safety and take control over your life. Trauma can be both physical and psychological; however, we are referring to psychological trauma here. The power of the mind-body connection is on full display when we observe that physical trauma can cause psychological trauma, and psychological trauma can cause physical health issues.

Stress is a heightened state of tension and alertness in your body and mind, triggered by life's challenges. On the bright side, stress can help you with focus and motivation. However, stress, when not properly managed, can lead to anxiety, depression, body tension, sleep issues, fatigue, headaches, chronic pain, heart and digestive issues, as well as many other health issues. As you can see, both trauma and stress have very negative effects on your life and well-being. Trauma and stress can come from various sources, such as vehicle accidents, abuse, violence, relationships, work, school, life changes, financial issues, and health problems, just to name a few. They can affect your relationship quality, employment, education, and all of your day-to-day experiences. Trauma can lead to stress, and stress can lead to trauma. As neither can be avoided entirely, the trick is to learn better ways to respond to them to preserve your peace.

Fortunately, our bodies were made with an all-natural healing energy. Once you learn the fundamentals, you can utilize all of it This book aims to provide curious souls like you with a foundational understanding of Somatic Therapy. It will give you practical knowledge of the tools and techniques used to heal the imbalances caused by your past wounds and aid in cultivating a life of lasting joy. The focal point will be learning the basics of awakening all of your body's potential. You will learn how to access your body's self-healing nature right now.

It's not magic.

It's science.

It's important to remember that self-healing means won't always have a therapist or a friend to guide you. It means doing the work on your own for yourself when no one is looking. It's time to learn a little more about these life-changing techniques.

Somatic Therapy is an approach to psychotherapy and natural medicine that genuinely understands how to unlock the full healing potential of the human body. It emphasizes the awareness of bodily sensations and movements as a gateway to understanding and healing emotional and psychological concerns. Somatic Therapy is a restorative intervention to address your psychological, emotional, or behavioral problems through professional guidance, support, and evidence-based techniques.

Many of these techniques have been utilized for over three thousand years and have been PROVEN to boost healing.

According to research, Bloch-Atefi and Smith Melbourne (2015) found that Somatic Therapy techniques are an effective and safe means of addressing trauma and stress-related complications. Brom et al. (2017) found that a Somatic Therapy technique effectively treated PTSD and other traumas. Despite all of the benefits, some people still shy away from treatments they haven't heard of or experienced. Others are skeptical by thinking, "It sounds too good to be true," or they may doubt the science by saying, "Insurance would cover it if it actually worked."

I've heard many reasons why people have yet to explore Somatic Therapy. If you have ever questioned whether Somatic Therapy can help you or your loved ones, don't worry; the answer is yes!

Even if you've experienced severe trauma, the answer is YES!

This is because the true nature of all life is to grow.

You can improve ANYTHING by pursuing a deeper understanding, committing to the process, and enhancing your brain connections. This is the core of Somatic Therapy.

Chronic mental and physical health issues usually indicate that you have some sort of imbalance within. It could be a biological, neurological, emotional, energy (chi), mental, or spiritual variance that needs to be balanced. In this book, you will learn how to improve these areas.

Here is a list of some conditions and concerns Somatic Therapy could help:

- Trauma-related disorders, including PTSD

- Anxiety disorders

- Depression

- Stress-related conditions

- Chronic pain and pain management

- Emotional dysregulation

- Attachment issues, including codependency

- Somatization disorder (Persistent physical symptoms without apparent medical cause)

- Body image & self-esteem concerns (Kiepe et al., 2012)

- Eating disorders including bulimia, binge eating, anorexia,

- Substance abuse and addiction

- Dissociative disorders (Rothschild, 2000)

- Sleep disturbances

- Relationship difficulties

- Chronic fatigue syndrome

- Grief and loss

- Sexual dysfunction

- Psychosomatic conditions

- Self-harm behaviors

- Reproductive health concerns, including infertility, prenatal and postnatal issues
  (Marlock et al., 2015, p. 332)

- Other chronic illnesses, including Fibromyalgia (Allmer et al., 2009).

These techniques hold significant power regardless of your age or the complexity of your trauma. It's entirely understandable if you feel your pain is too intricately embedded to ever improve, seemingly inseparable from your life. I'm here to show you that it is never too late nor too soon, and no wound is too deep to be healed naturally.

Somatic Therapy is a holistic approach that recognizes the interconnectedness of the body and mind in the healing process. The term holistic means that we have to consider the whole person. It focuses on the "embodied" experience of an individual, acknowledging that trauma and stress are not solely confined to the mind but also deeply rooted in the physical body.

In Somatic Therapy, "embodied" refers to the state of being FULLY present and aware of your sensations, bodily experiences and emotions. It involves connecting with and accessing information from the body. By working directly with the body, Somatic Therapy aims to release and resolve the stored stress and trauma while promoting healing and happiness.

As you know, traumatic experiences can leave a profound impact on both the mind and physical body. When faced with a traumatic event, the body activates the fight-or-flight or freeze response, releasing stress hormones to prepare you for immediate action (McCarty, 2016, Chapter 4). While your body's stress response exists to serve the good purpose of helping you cope with a coming threat, excessive or prolonged stress is deadly. Our bodies have a stress-based economic system that performs a delicate balancing act. A more precise term for your stress response system could be the resource allocation system, which furnishes the materials and supplies required for survival in a stressful situation. The stress response is one of the quickest physiological reactions your body undergoes, activating within a fraction of a second upon perceiving a threat.

Suppose the threat cannot be effectively addressed. In that case, the energy remains trapped within the body, leading to symptoms such as chronic pain, tension, hypervigilance, and even conditions like Fibromyalgia. Fibromyalgia is an extreme example of how psychological trauma could relate to a physical disability. It is a persistant condition marked by widespread hypervigilance with musculoskeletal pain, fatigue, sleep disturbances, and cognitive difficulties. Symptoms often include amplified sensitivity to pain, headaches, and irritable bowel syndrome (Arnold et al., 2011). It is theorized as being associated with the body being "stuck" in fight-or-flight mode.

Hypervigilance is a heightened state of sensory and psychological alertness characterized by an excessive and persistent "scanning" of the environment for possible threats or dangers. It's frequently related to anxiety, trauma, or post-traumatic stress disorder (PTSD), along with an increased sensitivity to sights and sounds, as well as an overwhelming sense of being constantly on guard.

Keep in mind, you do not need to have a chronic illness or any known illness to benefit from Somatic Therapy. Anyone, regardless of age, sex, and stress level, can enjoy the natural healing benefits it offers.

An often used Somatic Therapy technique is Somatic Experiencing® or SE®, developed by Dr. Peter A. Levine. SE® focuses on redirecting and releasing the trapped energy inside your body associated with traumatic experiences (Levine, 2010). Gradually exposing you to traumatic memories or sensations in small amounts (Brom et al., 2017). SE® allows for a safe and regulated exploration of the body's response. This facilitates the release of stored tension and restores a sense of safety.

Another approach is Sensorimotor Psychotherapy, developed by Pat Ogden, which integrates body-oriented techniques with talk therapy (Choosing Therapy, 2022). This approach helps you notice and regulate bodily sensations, create a more empathetic relationship with your body, and cultivate new patterns of movement and behavior (Ogden et al., 2006).

Somatic Therapy is particularly relevant when addressing trauma and stress because it goes beyond simply talking about the traumatic event. It acknowledges that trauma has direct physical manifestations. By releasing stored tension, Somatic Therapy will offer you an opportunity to heal at a deeper level (BioBeats, 2021). This can help you unleash a profound shift from within changing the relationship with not only yourself but the world around you.

The key to success lies in taking control of your own healing, as no one else can do it for you. You will have to commit both effort and time to yourself to make this work. This might mean getting up extra early, staying up late, or missing your favorite show to make room for your new healing lifestyle.

If you are currently in talk therapy, we'll discuss integrating these body-oriented techniques for the most significant benefits.

I hope you are excited to explore the art and science of Somatic Therapy as you unlock the door to a meaningful personal transformation like I did. I hope you now yearn for a deeper understanding of your true nature in a world where the mind and body are frequently regarded as separate entities. Get ready to start your journey to peace through self-discovery and harness the deep wisdom that resides within your very being.

Before we continue, I know you are excited to learn more about the BLESSING of Somatic Therapy in greater detail. However, let me first give you an overview of what you can expect in this book.

Book contents and purpose

This book has a little bit of everything. This is so you can build up your foundation knowledge before exploring your chosen path in more detail. We'll examine breathwork, grounding, somatic, and movement techniques.

Additionally, we'll explore essential and universally accepted concepts such as consciousness and mindfulness. You'll learn how to prepare yourself before treatment and how to find a therapist when you are ready.

When starting any Somatic Therapy, it is important to understand the basics of how your body responds to stress, especially your brain. There is enough happening in your body during stress to fill thousands of textbooks. Don't worry. This is not intended to be a scientific journal, so you won't be overwhelmed with every minute of empirical detail. I believe you will better appreciate your healing by knowing the biology and chemistry of it all. You'll learn enough details of this science to be knowledgeable about the processes. We'll also explore the mind-body connection, neurons, and the nervous system. I'll explain how you can "rewire" your brain.

We'll go over the practices vital to "discovering" yourself and how to merge self-care into your everyday habits and routines. We'll also discuss potential lifestyle changes and exercises needed for maximum healing. Next, we'll explore alternative medicines and therapies, such as one of my favorite areas, Ayurveda, to enhance the somatic changes. Everything you need to start your natural healing journey using Somatic

Therapy techniques is included. The best part is that you can

reach true and observable healing without prescription medications!

(Those currently taking or recommended to take prescriptions should continue following their doctor's orders).

This book informs and better prepares you to decide which therapy is best suited for you and to help you develop a daily healing routine.

This book is not intended to train you to be a therapist or practitioner of these complex techniques. The practitioners and therapists specializing in these methods have completed hundreds if not thousands of hours of training and practical experiences. Their guidance is irreplaceable in this process.

This book was created for those new to the topic or those who just don't "get" this intricate and complex field. While Somatic Therapy alone might not relieve all your pain, anxiety, and stress, it is a significant piece of the healing puzzle.

This book is for anyone who tosses and turns all night with racing thoughts, those whose bodies are screaming at them from the inside out, and anyone seeking peace or relaxation.

This can be an intimidating topic full of terminology and concepts foreign to many, just as it was for me many years ago. It is disheartening to see complex vocabulary and concepts become barriers to someone's healing, which is why I created this book.

Keywords are written in straightforward, general terms so a beginner can breathe easily. I've tried to make it painless to understand. You do not have to be familiar with this subject, although there may be some terms you must look up independently.

Everything is broken down into plain terms, leaving you with a complete understanding of every bit needed to start your journey to wholeness.

Some themes are repeated throughout the book. Remember that this repetition happens because everything is interconnected or related in a never-ending life cycle. You will learn similar concepts from different perspectives and angles to provide a comprehensive understanding.

Somatic Therapy gives a distinct strategy to healthcare that many in the West know little about. Given time, guidance, and practice, you will learn to acknowledge and relax areas of tension, discomfort, or restricted body movement connected to stress and unresolved trauma. I know you can find the solace your mind and body crave.

It's time to continue your journey toward self-discovery and relief.

I'd like to share my firsthand testimonial about how somatic and complementary practices saved my life.

All healing starts with self-healing.

My story and why this can change your whole being

My name is Naty, creator of Naty H.E.A.L.S.com.

Naty is what my most loved friends and family call me.

H.E.A.L.S. stands for Healing Enlightened Awakened Light Souls.

I am a spiritual teacher, Ayurveda medicine practitioner, Reiki Master, ordained minister, author, content creator, and podcaster.

But above all, I am a woman, mother, wife, sister, cousin, aunt and daughter.

I've dedicated my life to being a mental health and chronic illness advocate. My passion is to help others find healing and motivation while living a more purposeful life. I share my story now to show that healing is possible for anyone, even after experiencing extreme trauma and pain in my own life. Studying somatic and complementary practices has allowed me to do things that I never thought I'd be able to do again.

My parents, a Puerto Rican musician father and a Mexican Christian mother, raised me as a first-generation American. My mother raised us as a single mom within her large family. I grew up on farms in South New Jersey, where I lived in low-income housing and faced poverty. English was not my first language. As a child, I often played in the blueberry fields, running through the sprinklers that watered the plants. Unfortunately, my exposure to unknown chemicals during this time had an additional adverse effect on my nervous system.

I was traumatized frequently, starting at a young age, by severe childhood bullying, sexual assault, and physical abuse, as well as other forms of abuse. My reality has been molded by several tragic events. My "normal" was to be in a never-ending fight, flight or freeze response. When I was a young child with undiagnosed neurodivergence, I had no idea why I was different. My gut feeling just told me that I was. Regardless, I was expected to "act normal" at all times. I mastered how to mask my traumas and emotions and how to hold it all in.

One very traumatizing event occurred when I was eleven years old. I was involved in an automobile accident that killed my stepfather in front of my eyes and seriously injured my mother. I broke my clavicle and three ribs in the crash. I also needed numerous stitches for my scalp. After what I witnessed that night and given that my mother was in a coma for a long time, I was unsure if she would live or die. I had to move in with other family members while she healed from multiple operations and a four-month-long hospital stay due to her horrific injuries. She managed to survive by loving grace. By the time I was 12, I frequently had panic attacks as a result of my untreated trauma. My family doctor swiftly prescribed anxiety/depression medicine. These drugs were supposed to help me, but instead, they left me a numb addict, which ended up robbing me of most of my independence. I also became addicted to running from my feelings. I spent the rest of my childhood and young adulthood battling extreme anxiety and depressive episodes. I feared driving or riding in any vehicle, especially on highways. I was constantly afraid that death was just around the corner. I would even panic upon hearing certain noises, like sirens from emergency vehicles, until adulthood.

Due to my family dynamics, no one knew about my daily struggles; I had to keep it to myself. Everyone must have thought that the medicines should have been enough for me, but in reality, they were just part of my downfall. There were times when I couldn't see a future and moments when I didn't want one. I was told to pray my trauma away, but despite this, the physical pain and aches I started to feel continued regularly. Every day, I was also battling with stomach issues and migraines. The pain grew greater during my adolescent years, especially after my father committed suicide. It was sad that I understood his reasoning as I also struggled with deep sadness, anxiety, and recurrent suicidal thoughts. As a busy single mom of three, I didn't understand exactly what I was feeling or how it would affect the rest of my life, but I knew one thing: I was broken and resentful.

In the '90s, I was diagnosed with Post Traumatic Stress Disorder and Bipolar Disorder; however, I didn't understand what they were. The adults in my culture looked down upon mental illness and knew very little about mental healthcare. I was still on my own when dealing with my issue. It was challenging to figure out the mental healthcare system independently, and I had very few resources to even try. At the time, I didn't have a smartphone or internet access at home.

I became a mother of three at a very young age; I faced so much **stress as a single mother.** I had to use everything I learned until this point: to fake it until I made it. It was tough to raise them in poverty, but our love for each other provided me the motivation needed to recover and save my life.

All of my children were born by c-section, which further harmed my already delicate nervous system and body. I was now severely dependent on painkillers to make it through each day. This was "normal," considering the knowledge available to me in my environment then. The c-sections, along with other traumatic experiences and abuse, caused my body to completely break down. In my lifetime, I've undergone 11 operations and been in 4 serious car accidents. Throughout my twenties, I suffered from a host of medical issues, including Fibromyalgia, Endometriosis, Gastroparesis, Psoriatic Arthritis, migraines, liver and kidney problems, and diabetes. Unfortunately, despite the many doctor visits and hospital stays, no one seemed to know how to effectively alleviate my symptoms. Then, at the age of 26, cancer cells were discovered on my cervix, almost two years after my hysterectomy. The medication prescribed by doctors had severe side effects and landed me back in the hospital for a week. It wasn't until I sought the help of a holistic natural medicine practitioner and made significant changes to my diet that the cancer cells eventually vanished.

As the years passed, my life became even more complicated due to a series of toxic and abusive relationships, the addiction to pain medication, as well as my struggles with codependency and abandonment issues.

I was repeating the generational traumas of my ancestors.

I was often an angry and miserable person.

I treated myself like I was worthless.

I sometimes treated those around me poorly.

Until then, I felt like I had been at WAR my entire life.

By my early thirties, I had a spiritual awakening.

This was the time that I realized that I was an addict and my life was a mess.

I needed to make a change.

I slowly stopped relying on prescription medications and turned to natural remedies, including water healing and spiritual baths, to relieve my pain. With determination and a focus on self-healing, I began to recover and rediscover myself.

However, I was still not comfortable in my body because of the fatigue, muscle cramps, and body aches that my fight-flight-or-freeze mode caused by being "stuck on."

My decision to concentrate on learning somatic healing and spirituality marked my turning point. I quit binge-watching hours of reality TV and started spending my days learning positive things. I spent all my days doing research, one issue at a time. I started incorporating breathwork into my life. I began to find comfort and solace in grounding. Recently, I had an unfortunate incident. I fractured the L2 of my lumbar spine and had to rely even more on my body's natural healing abilities. I'm grateful that I was already familiar with these techniques, as I undoubtedly would be taking prescription painkillers today. My closest pals are now Somatic Therapy, reiki, yoga, breathwork, and meditation. They are the key to my vitality.

There's something truly wondrous that happens during my daily mind-body connection routine. I am awestruck. In my own internal experience, in my most settled, quiet moments of consciousness, I find myself awestruck by what happens in and around me. I experienced things that I once thought were sorcery or witchcraft. I now understand these experiences represent the unlocking of my full potential. This is not magic it is science. Now, my mind becomes completely still and alert. I notice things such as time going by faster than usual, and my anxieties from stress, chronic illness, PTSD, and other issues are gone in those moments. I feel great unity and peace with the world around me. After a lifetime of limiting my awareness or praying to not be aware, it was the gaining of awareness that saved my life.

One of the keys to my practice was learning to manage my "lower self," which encompasses my mind, intellect, and ego, using emotional regulation. I needed this because my ego, residing in my lower self, was getting in the way of my progress. I discovered that I had to give myself permission to surrender my ego to connect to my "higher self," aka my most enlightened authentic self, to heal. What sticks out to me is what happens after I utilize the techniques. I improved both physically and mentally in managing my Fibromyalgia symptoms and my fractured spine. I am experiencing less pain daily.

This is a real solution to real problems.

There were moments when I could not get out of bed or even go to the restroom on my own. I can now walk farther and longer distances than ever before. I am swimming, driving some, setting boundaries, eating better, sleeping better, and loving more. Thanks to Somatic Therapy and other natural healing techniques, I can now be the person I was always meant to be. With patience, I've found more peace with myself. My life has completely changed into what I could never even dream of as a child and young adult.

Even with all of the trauma and abuse I've endured, I am grateful for the experiences that have shaped my life. I've created a life full of love and abundance while pursuing my dreams. I have my life back. I am dedicated to helping you discover your path to healing and self-love by sharing the tools and support I wished I had when I began my own journey. If you are wondering if I still experience pain or symptoms from all of these ailments, the answer is yes. The difference is that I now have the tools to emotionally and spiritually to deal with it. I no longer let it drag me down into depression or up into mania; I can better regulate my emotions. I pray that you can see that healing is possible for anyone, regardless of the issue, financial ability, or cultural background. I hope my story encourages you to push forward and commit to natural healing.

Now, it's time to learn some foundational concepts of Somatic Therapy, the mind-body connection, resilience, and neuroplasticity.

Mind-Body?!?! Huh?

You may wonder what someone means when they say "the mind-body connection.

The mind-body connection is the inseparable bridge between thoughts, emotions, and your body. Your mental and emotional condition can influence your physical health and vice versa.

Emotions guide you, informing your decisions, motivations, and responses. They carry the force to fire up your passion, boost your connections, or unravel your harmony.

Emotions can lighten or darken you from the inside out. The practice of embracing and understanding your feelings will allow you to navigate life with empathy and authenticity. You will open pathways to compassion, vulnerability, intimacy, peace, and love.

In this life, you have autonomy, meaning you are self-directed and can engage in self-correction practices. Your true motivations are revealed by your day-to-day routine because we all gravitate toward what we think will give us the most pleasure. An example might be your desire for stability that turns into complacency. Some people are comfortable and safe being sad. This speaks to the idea that feeling down can be a source of stability. Complacency means that you are not willing to make the changes needed to heal because you think it feels safer where you are, reliving the same thing day after day. Remember that complacency only acts for your short-term self-satisfaction at the expense of your long-term success. It can not only deter you from starting therapy but also hinder your progress in therapy; for example, when you stop trying as much when you start to feel better. Watch out for your complacency. Suppose you have ever been hesitant about starting therapy because it's more comfortable to avoid discussing stress or trauma. In that case, this is your nervous system or emotional side making the decision. Or perhaps, after many sessions, you may start feeling better and forget that you still have work to do. Much of this work will require you to use your cognitive or rational side. In this example, rationally, you know that if the only two choices are 1. Stay the same and feel the same, or 2. Change and improve. 100% of people would want to improve. Yet, for some reason, our nervous system is in charge of making so many of our decisions. We stall, procrastinate, and are sometimes held back by our nervous system.

Adopt a new mindset and take a closer look into your daily practices. Learn to forge a better life and cultivate a richer, more meaningful reality. How you behave and feel can cascade out to your family and loved ones, who, in turn, can lay it on to others. Your healing can have a ripple effect as peace radiates out to those around you. Your healing is part of the greater purpose in this life.

The act of thinking and processing can soothe your mind and body from the effects of trauma and stress. The mind-body connection is pivotal in every aspect of your daily life.

Eastern philosophies have recognized this vital link for centuries, viewing the mind-body connection as an elemental aspect of human existence. Only in recent years has Western science begun to unravel this link's immense impact. Numerous studies have demonstrated the influence of psychological factors concerning various physical conditions. For instance, stress has been connected to a range of ailments, including cardiovascular disease, immune system dysfunction, and digestive disorders. Your mental state can also affect your pain perception, as seen in chronic conditions such as Fibromyalgia.

A rare condition that nicely illustrates the mind-body connection is Cataplexy. People with this condition can lose muscle control simply by being too excited, having a good laugh, or getting scared (Lima et al., 2019). They can completely collapse for a brief period (Dauvilliers et al., 2014).

Also, did you know there is a condition called Takotsubo Cardiomyopathy, often called broken heart syndrome?

It's caused by powerful emotions or physical distress that temporarily disrupts heart function and can mimic heart attack symptoms. These symptoms are not caused by blocked arteries; the heart's left ventricle weakens suddenly due to a surge in stress hormones (Scantlebury & Prasad, 2014). Emotional distress like loss or extreme stress is often linked to this condition. Luckily, this syndrome is reversible, with symptoms subsiding in weeks to months (Akashi et al., 2008).

The mind-body connection is especially crucial in the field of trauma healing. As stated before, traumatic experiences can become physically trapped within the body, leading to various adverse symptoms. The traumatic event leaves an impression on your brain and also on your body's cells! To make matters worse, this trauma can then be "reactivated" when something similar occurs, putting your body through the trauma once again. We'll address trauma in more detail in Chapter 7.

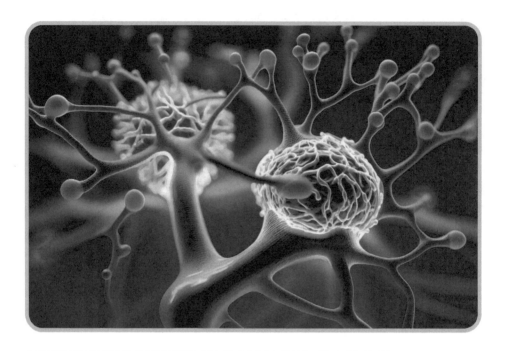

Elasticity with Neuroplasticity

The mind-body connection is tightly linked with neuroplasticity. This is the brain's capacity to restructure itself and form new neural connections throughout your lifespan. This means that your thoughts and experiences can actually reshape your brain's structure and function. Neural connections are also referred to as synapses. These connections allow your brain cells, called neurons, to communicate with each other. The pattern in these connections is constantly changing. All of your experiences are imprinted in the structure and functioning of your brain. As Carla Shatz paraphrased Donald Hebb's principle (Hebb, 1988), "Neurons that fire together wire together." ("The Developing Brain on JSTOR," n.d.)

As a response to this neural firing, our reality is created.

Channeling the power of neuroplasticity through techniques like mindfulness, meditation, and visualization can actively reshape your neural pathways, promoting positive changes in your mental and physical health. You may have often encountered the term 'mindfulness' without fully grasping its meaning (Choosing Therapy, 2023). To clarify, it is the practice of focusing on the now with curiosity and non-judgment, bringing awareness to your thoughts, feelings, and sensations (Marlock et al., 2015, p. 402). This will encourage a sense of calm and clarity that we'll cover in more detail in the coming chapters.

Neurobiological research has shed light on the remarkable effectiveness of Somatic Therapy. It has been shown that you can stimulate your brain's ability to adapt and heal through somatic techniques (Marlock et al., 2015, p. 126). Through these techniques, you can generate fresh neural connections while strengthening the connections you already have. The goal of these techniques is to create brain-derived neurotrophic factor known as BDNF. BDNF is a protein that supports neural growth and facilitates learning. You can increase your BDNF levels by reducing stress, inflammation, exercise, and positive social interactions. You will use this increased BDNF to rewire your brain for healing and resilience (How to Increase BDNF: 10 Ways to Rescue Your Brain, 2020).

After all your stress-reducing, inflammation-fighting, exercising, and being social, what should you do with the increase in BDNF?

Try the following exercises:

Learning a new skill or hobby:

Engaging in activities such as painting, learning a new language, or practicing a sport will challenge your brain and boost the formation of new neural pathways.

Brain teasers and puzzles:

Activities that involve problem-solving, such as crosswords, puzzles or riddles, can stimulate the creation of new neural connections.

Learning through technology:

Brain training apps or software can provide exercises and activities specifically aimed at helping form new neural connections and improving cognitive function.

Music engagement:

Developing your ability to play a musical instrument requires concentration, coordination, and memory. This promotes the creation of new neural connections.

While doing these activities may not seem related to your Somatic Therapy, they are all a part of it. Rewiring your pathways and forming new connections is precisely what we have our sights on.

The secret lies in immersing your brain with new experiences.

Every thought counts!

Now that you know the mind-body connection, it's time to cultivate a STRONG link for the most effective healing. There are many significant concepts to building this connection, which every single person looking into Somatic Therapy needs to know. These concepts include self-awareness, the true self, authenticity, and emotional regulation.

Ever wonder what exactly is meant by the term "self-awareness"?

Self-awareness is the true understanding and honest recognition of your feelings, thoughts, and conduct. It involves being conscious of your internal experiences, values, abilities, and areas that need improvement. A well-balanced amount of self-awareness is essential for your emotional regulation, decision-making, healthy relationships, and resilience. Many of us live busy or chaotic lives full of distractions, including our phones, TVs, and computers. Trauma and stress has made it hard for many to face reality or even want to be aware of their emotions. Turning to life-numbing substances or anything that can block out the pain or stress is often seen as easier or as the only option. It sometimes feels effortless to block out trauma and pain by pretending that it doesn't bother you, and some even flat-out deny its very existence. Unfortunately, this technique is the opposite of being self-aware. It will never lead to healing or a life of lasting joy.

The somatic healing process will involve you purposefully un-distracting your mind and actually processing your thoughts and emotions. The journey ahead may be difficult and even painful, but it will undoubtedly be worth it. Ultimately, you will look back and be thankful for the rest of your life. By taking the time to develop your self-awareness, you will gain clarity, authenticity, and the ability to make conscious choices that match your true self. Only then will be able to let down the "masks" you have taught yourself to wear. The ones that protected you from the judgment of others.

The goal of all of the "awareness" examples and exercises in this book is intended not just to build any type of awareness but a quality awareness.

Quality awareness is an accurate awareness.

To have high-quality awareness, you must reduce stress and dysfunction enough to have an authentic fact-based response instead of a trauma-based reaction. This part will not happen overnight after years or decades of living and thinking a certain way.

This takes time; however, you are worth the effort.

Self-awareness does not only aid your psychological health but also your physical health. How many people do you know who simply ignore cues from the body by calling them "normal"? Practicing the self-awareness exercises in this book will enable you to recognize and address subtle signals from your body that aren't "normal." This heightened

awareness can allow for discovery of possible health problems early enough for the most effective treatment

> "The mind is not a vessel to be filled but a fire to be kindled." - Plutarch
>
> Plutarch Quotes. n.d.

True self and authenticity

When you improve your self-awareness, you can find your true self.

When someone uses the term your "true self," they refer to your core identity, which includes the parts of you that are just there regardless of what friends, family, or the culture around you believe.

These are your values, such as honesty and punctuality, purpose, skills, gender/sexual orientation, etc. Authenticity is when you can actively live in a way that matches this core identity: your true self. It's when your words, behaviors, and actions mirror who you really are. Authenticity means admitting your mistakes when you are wrong without defending them. Being authentic is about self-discovery and self-acceptance. It involves shedding societal expectations and daring to embrace your true essence. Being authentic is a courageous act of embracing your imperfections and celebrating your uniqueness (Christian, 2023).

A person living without authenticity would be someone hiding their feelings, thoughts, and behaviors from others for various reasons, such as shame or wanting to fit in. A typical example experienced worldwide is when people hide their sexual identity and sexual orientation, which are fundamental aspects of a person's true self and are not a conscious choice. Meaning these are natural internal patterns that tell the brain what it desires. Although sexual identity and sexual orientation are components of your core identity, many people hide it due to family or societal expectations. Just imagine the stress and trauma that hiding something this significant can cause to a person's emotional and physical health. Many live a life of fear of harassment or anxiety due to violence against the LGBTQIA community. The fear, anxiety, shame, or guilt one feels can lead to depression, isolation, or even thoughts of self-harm and suicide.

With this example, you can see how finding your true self and authentically living is central to anyone wanting to find peace.

Better self-awareness also leads to better emotional regulation. The ultimate goal of emotional regulation, aka self-regulation, is the ability to manage and adjust your emotions effectively when you need it most. This is learning how to cope. It means that you can be upset and still be respectful. It means you can be "triggered" and still not treat others poorly. It's learning to solve conflicts productively and involves recognizing, understanding, and controlling emotional responses in a balanced manner. This skill will enable you to navigate life's challenges, maintain emotional stability, and make thoughtful decisions. Emotional self-regulation promotes a joyful life as you will have healthier relationships (Christian, 2023).

Chapter 3 will cover a range of techniques to help you live with authenticity and come closer to your true self. In the next section, we'll focus on the process of changing your self-limiting perspectives.

"Happiness is not something ready-made. It comes from your own actions."
— Dalai Lama (Dalai Lama Quotes. n.d.)

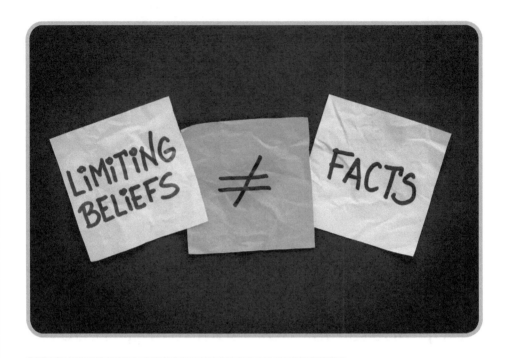

Self-limiting perspectives

Your beliefs, attitudes, and perceptions influence your health and overall life experience. Your perception is the way you understand and interpret the world around you. It's how you comprehend and translate the experiences, sensations, emotions, and information from your senses. Your perception is significantly shaped by traumatic experiences and can be highly self-limiting. An accurate perception is critical to healing, as misperceptions can dramatically impact your treatment. For example, suppose you have been interpreting a strained and painful muscle in your back as a physical injury. However, in Somatic Therapy, it is discovered to be connected to moments of high stress or tension. In this example, your perception caused you to be unaware of the root cause of your pain.

I, too, grew up with a misperception about how the mind-body connection worked. I was taught that my body belonged to me, but my mind belonged to God. My perception was that if something terrible happened to my body, it was a punishment from God. I'm sure you can see how this perception could have limited my treatment. Developing and enhancing your perception will keep you on the right path to healing. Remember that sometimes your viewpoints can set you up for failure.

A typical example is when individuals refuse to attempt therapy because they believe their trauma is too severe. They convince themselves that recovery is impossible. This lack of confidence is self-limiting and is often used as justification to give up and surrender to the pain. True self-confidence comes from embracing your growth, accepting your imperfections, having faith in your higher self, and recognizing the progress you have already achieved.

Self-limiting perspectives can be any thought or outlook that restricts or limits you from pursuing what you need or want. We all have biases ingrained into our being starting at birth. Your family-societal conditioning and cultural narratives play a significant role in Somatic Therapy. We are all molded by the families we are born into and the society around us.

Some examples of these would be thoughts that start with "I'm too old for," "I'm too young to try," "I'm too dumb to talk about," and "I'm too weak for."

Try to imagine what you would believe if you could magically take away the influence of the culture/family around you. These beliefs, biases, and perspectives can not only be a barrier to your natural healing but also hold you back in life. These false beliefs must be shed before you start your healing journey.

> "No legacy is so rich as honesty."
> ~ William Shakespeare (William Shakespeare Quotes. n.d.)

Somatic Therapy will help you overcome beliefs that are holding you back. Your upbringing, community beliefs, and cultural norms shape your perceptions, emotions, and bodily experiences. As you learned, some of your viewpoints are false. You should focus on unraveling these ingrained patterns to overcome these false beliefs. Participating in Somatic Therapy will enable your true self to take control, transform these limiting beliefs, and allow you to embrace new narratives that promote wholeness, authenticity, and embodiment.

Many of these self-limiting beliefs are held within your subconscious mind. You will need to challenge any negative self-talk and thoughts to make progress. You will always create whatever your words are, as your inner dialog is where you live. For example, I used to believe that my worthiness was tied to my achievements and the approval of others, especially my family. In some ways, their thoughts and feelings were more important than my own. This limiting belief left me feeling constantly stressed, anxious, and disconnected from my true self. Through gentle body-centered practices and the guidance of my talk therapist, I learned to reconnect with my body, listen to its wisdom, and release stored emotions.

I shed layers of self-doubt with each session and gradually embraced my inherent worthiness. Through therapy, I learned that I was no longer just trying to survive; I was doing and thriving regardless of what others thought.

Somatic Therapy equipped me to recognize that my value lies within me, independent of external validation.

I now live authentically, free from the confines of limiting beliefs. I made room for self-acceptance and joy. My life has dramatically changed since I simply started believing in myself and living authentically.

Stop now and take a few minutes to reflect on your negative self-talk and thoughts.

Think about what's holding you back from living authentically.

Identify a belief that could hold you back from natural healing.

If you are unsure of the answers, it's OK. Your trained practitioner can guide you.

I've included exercises designed to help you realize your generational limiting beliefs in the companion book, "The Blessing: Workbook and Journal of Life with Gratitude."

A great way to discover some of the subconscious beliefs holding you back is through somatic inquiry. A few somatic inquiry techniques include body scanning, breathwork, and body awareness.

These techniques can open you up to shifting your limiting beliefs

We'll cover these in more detail in chapters 3 and 5; however, here are two examples.

Embodied affirmations:

Repeating affirmations like "I am safe, I am loved, I am protected" while feeling the stability of your bare feet on the ground can strengthen a sense of security and connection. Don't just say the words. Let the meaning of them really sink into your soul.

Body-centered visualization and guided imagery:

Try to imagine yourself standing tall, rooted to the ground like a sturdy tree. Visualize golden rays of light entering the top of your head, moving down throughout your body, nourishing every cell. You might sense a cozy, embracing warmth washing over you, leaving you feeling revitalized and deeply relaxed. This will help you feel rejuvenated and refreshed.

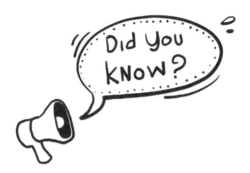

Trauma is not just in your head; it's in your nervous system, tissues, and body. Somatic Therapy acknowledges this truth and provides a path for healing from the inside out.

YOUR BODY CAN DO IT IT IS TIME TO CONVINCE YOUR MIND

Chapter 2: Deeper Understanding of Somatic Therapy

What to expect in this chapter:

More on Somatic Therapy
Mindset for treatment
15 types of Somatic Therapy techniques
Benefits and Constraints of Somatic Therapy

What is Somatic Therapy & why it's so important?

Somatic, in simple terms, refers to the body and physical sensations. "Somatic" refers to anything related to the body, separate from the mind or spirit. It can refer to sensations, actions, or functions that occur in the body. For example, somatic symptoms are physical symptoms that originate from within the body. Somatic Therapy relates to the recognition and perception of how your body feels, moves, and responds. It involves paying attention to these bodily sensations to accumulate intelligence into your emotions, health, and mind-body connection.

When you are mad or upset, have you ever wondered why your shoulders or neck start to ache? Or you may all of a sudden get a stomach ache or headache.

This is the mind-body connection at work.

So, you already know the basics that your mind and body are not only connected physically but emotionally, spiritually, and mentally. We'll now explore specific therapy techniques in more detail.

Imagine a dance between your body and mind, where your breath's rhythm orchestrates your soul's movements.

Your physique has its own language, and Somatic Therapy speaks it fluently. It recognizes that your body is not just a container for navigating life but an intricate map of your experiences and emotions. It understands that your muscles, bones, and even the subtlest sensations can hold the key to your healing.

At its core, Somatic Therapy invites you to become a curious explorer of your own physicality. It encourages you to tune into faint hints within your body, the gentle hum of tension in your chest, or the shakes of excitement in your belly. It will help you decode the stories etched in your muscles and nerves. It will give a voice to your unspoken truths.

By engaging in techniques such as breathwork, gentle movement, and touch, you will gradually peel away the coat of armor that has unconsciously built up. You will summon vulnerability and relief into your life.

Somatic Therapy is a chance to rewrite your narrative, just as I have.

You will face the past while you create new possibilities for yourself in the present and future. It will show you that healing lies in analyzing your thoughts and feelings AND embracing the wisdom held within your body. Through this unification of body, spirit, and mind you will awaken your natural capacity for peace and joy.

Connecting with your bodily impulses and its intuitive wisdom involves honoring your body's natural intelligence. You will tap into a root wisdom that will guide you towards making optimal life choices and having authentic life experiences.

You are now joining the community of Somatic Therapy practitioners and students, where there are no strangers, only fellow explorers.

Let your body guide you to self-discovery, one step, one sensation at a time.

Take another deep breath, and let's move to the mindset needed for treatment.

"Adversity is the first path to truth."
– Lord Byron   (Lord Byron Quotes. n.d.)

Resilience: How I Outwork Murphy's Law... Most of the Time

Your time on earth will include rotations of pain and peace, just as the daylight turns to night. How long you live in these cycles is partly dependent on your actions. Having thoughts and emotions of compassion, gratefulness, and positivity during hardship will always bring you closer to harmony and healing. Your ability to maintain this outlook will show your actual toughness, otherwise known as resilience. Resilience is a strength and skill that you hold deep within yourself and is how your ancestors survived so many obstacles. It encompasses your mental, emotional, and behavioral ability to bounce back, adapt, and recover from internal and external challenges, setbacks, and adversity.

Different types of resilience relate to your Somatic Therapy.

Emotional Resilience:

How sensitive you are to change and how you cope with emotional stress. How you handle your emotions positively and healthily. For example, someone who recently lost a job will reach out to a trusted loved one to talk, participate in self-care, and write in their journal instead of being overwhelmed with sadness.

Psychological Resilience:

While emotional resilience is focused on how effectively you recognize and handle your emotions, psychological resilience involves your motivation, problem-solving, and goal-setting.

For example, someone who recently lost a job takes this as an opportunity to learn a new skill or start a new business instead of being overwhelmed with despair.

Physical Resilience:

Your body's ability to adapt to change and maintain strength and stamina. It's how efficiently and quickly you recover from challenges like illness or accidents.

For example, someone with a mobility issue may dedicate themselves to a recovery plan focusing on strength and agility.

They maintain a positive outlook instead of giving up. It's only through dedication to the plan and the ability to adjust to physical challenges that mobility is restored.

Resilience means maintaining a positive attitude, finding inner strength, and learning valuable lessons from difficult experiences. It is not how well you avoid pain and suffering but rather your capacity to work through it. It's about reframing your negative thoughts and utilizing the resources you have within and around you to better the situation. Resilience allows you to grow and flourish in spite of life's ups and downs. Without it, you cannot overcome your hardships and will be easily overwhelmed. Many individuals struggling with substance abuse or other addictions show a lack of resilience by relying on unhealthy coping mechanisms (Najavits, 2015).

For example, a study conducted by Alec Roy showed that people who attempted suicide had significantly lower resilience scores than those who had never made such attempts. It's important to note that your resilience can vary from situation to situation. For instance, you may be able to process a job loss better than when facing an illness. Something that may cause trauma in one person may not in another person based on their resilience. Common traits in highly resilient people include flexibility, versatility, and persistence. They often express more gratitude, forgiveness, acceptance, and compassion. The skill of resilience is pretty great to have, and you may be wondering how to enhance yours. Several factors can influence your resilience, including your self-esteem, emotional regulation, communication skills, types of coping mechanisms you choose, and other available support systems

(Roy et al., 2007). Things that offer you a feeling of purpose, build your confidence and self-worth, or connect you with others can build your resilience. Building resilience is not a one-shot and your done exercise; it takes time. You will need to work on this skill constantly. Now, it's time to start developing your mental and emotional fitness.

Let's talk about the resilience power booster of positive thinking.

On the bright side, positive emotions and a healthy mindset have been proven to enhance resilience, boost immune function, and promote faster recovery from illness and injury (How a Positive Mindset Boosts Your Health Short Course, n.d.).

We have all heard the phrase "think happy thoughts"; the truth is, there is real science behind it. Every day, when you wake up and open your eyes, you have a choice.

You can choose peace.

One little trick I use daily to boost my positivity is remembering to be grateful for something or someone at certain times of the day. Pick a time; any time will work; for example, upon waking, 11:11 a.m. or 4:44 p.m. I do this with some deep breaths before writing or doing any creative project. Use this special time to keep things in perspective each day. Everyone has something to be thankful for.

Please know that your thoughts are **ENERGY**, and you control if you want to add negative or positive energy to your body and daily life. Everything you do is based on this energy. It's important to note that your energy directly affects you and all other living things around you, including your plants.

A study by IKEA observed students giving positive and negative energy to plants by insulting or complimenting them. All other conditions, such as sunlight and water, remained the same. The plant receiving the negative energy wilted, while the one given positive energy thrived (marilisaraccoglobal, 2018).

(If you would like to learn more about this study, search for "Bully a Plant: Say no to Bullying online.")

If you pause and really think, this small act of gratitude can transition your focus away from low thoughts that deplete your energy to positive thoughts that can make your body and mind just feel better.

Yes, it can be that simple!

I recommend everyone start with this modest action today.

> "Do what you can, with what you have, where you are"
> – Theodore Roosevelt   (Theodore Roosevelt Quotes. n.d.)

A Healing Mind frame

It may seem obvious that improving something means changing it; however, many people resist the change part. Ironically, change is the only permanent fixture in life. All the techniques in this book are designed, tested, and researched to improve your life, so naturally, they will involve change. This means you cannot improve your health while clinging to the same old mindset. I understand everyone has preferences, and it may be uncomfortable to embrace new things. However, you must decide whether to leap into the unknown or stay in your current state.

Remember that what you're doing now will only get you the results that you now have. You will achieve different outcomes only by trying something novel and possibly uncomfortable.

The main thing that you should focus on is being WILLING.

Willing to reconsider things that you currently believe to be 100% true, such as "my mind will never be still enough to meditate" or "I will always feel this way."

Willing to view the world through a different lens.

Willing to commit to a mindfulness routine and self-care.

Willing to fully, openly, and honestly communicate.

Just being willing to change is all you need to get started.

With this new mindset, you will still be you; you'll just be a more peaceful and balanced version of yourself over time.

Tips to consider before therapy

Make sure you can invest the energy and time required for the process. Lack of commitment and motivation is a major barrier that is made significantly more complex for those with depression and other challenges.

Prepare emotionally, mentally, and spiritually to bring up and process painful memories (G. C. Center, 2020). Treatments often have a high dropout rate, possibly due to reliving the trauma or feeling overwhelmed.

Let the therapist know your comfort level regarding touch.

Be open to techniques that may seem "weird," "silly," or "different." Some methods you may associate as "just for hippies," and you may not relate to that; however, the hippies have peace and love figured out, so consider opening your mind to different experiences.

It's time for the therapies!

The information provided here is a rough guide to give you a general overview of therapy types and what to expect.

All prices and figures may differ from your therapist's price list and session recommendations.

Go with the program plan recommended by your therapist.

Since this is a beginner's book, only an overview of each approach is included. Nevertheless, enough information is provided to determine which therapy you want to explore going forward. I am not affiliated, sponsored, or endorsed by any trademark owners described. I am speaking from my personal experience and knowledge.

If you want to apply your health insurance to cover the costs, always check with your specific insurance policy first. Ask about coverage for each particular technique; be advised that many therapists do not directly bill insurance. If your plan has out-of-network coverage for these treatments, you must pay out of pocket first and then send receipts to the insurance company for reimbursement.

Keep in mind that you are unique, so the number of treatments required will vary widely, based on the following:

Condition you are trying to manage

The severity of your symptoms

Response of your body

Amount of time you dedicate to your mindfulness routine between sessions

While this is not an exhaustive or exclusive list, it comprises tried and tested foundational techniques that have shown outstanding results.

15 types of therapy (that have changed lives all around the world)

1. Sensorimotor Psychotherapy

Sensorimotor Psychotherapy is an appraoch to help you heal from trauma by combining talk therapy with body-based techniques (Choosing Therapy, 2022).

It emphasizes the link between the mind and body, using exercises to heighten awareness of your bodily sensations, emotions, and movements (Ogden et al., 2006). Sensorimotor Psychotherapy encourages a non-verbal conversation with your body. It listens to your muscles, the rhythms of your breath, and any subtle shifts. You will learn to separate the past from the present and future. This therapeutic approach will allow you to navigate your inner experiences without relying solely on words (Ogden et al., 2006).

The therapist will observe your body language, breathing patterns, and facial expressions to gain insights. For example, you can test this out yourself by noticing exactly when your body tenses up in certain situations or when you hold your breath when talking about a specific subject. Your body will reveal clues that you may not even be aware of. Clues that talk therapy alone might not pick up on, especially in the day and age of tele-therapy sessions (Ogden et al., 2006). This treatment is excellent for addressing the lingering physical sensations that can result from uncompleted stress responses during traumatic events, which may manifest as physical mannerisms or emotional struggles like anxiety and depression. The treatment aims to create a safe space for you to revisit and complete any unresolved actions related to the trauma. This can provide a sense of much-needed closure. Keep in mind that recalling specific details of the trauma is not always necessary to yield the desired results.

The therapy session typically follows three key steps:

Establishing a safe environment: This step lets you focus on your inner instincts, physical sensations, and feelings, in a protected setting. Recalling and integrating the trauma: When you are ready to discuss the painful experience, the therapist will guide you to pay attention to your emotional shifts and bodily responses during the recollection. Understanding the body's language helps in vividly recalling the trauma (Gunter & Bodner, 2008). Completing unfulfilled actions: This step involves assisting you to carry out any actions that may have been halted during the trauma. This could range from asserting yourself verbally to making physical movements in self-defense. By taking these actions and achieving these milestones, you can experience a feeling of victory and liberation from the grip of traumatic memories (Choosing Therapy, 2022).

Sensorimotor therapy will help you gain control over your responses to trauma activators, distinguish between back then and now, and be aware of thoughts and bodily sensations without becoming overwhelmed (Ogden et al., 2006). You must sustain a dual awareness state for sensorimotor therapy to yield positive outcomes. This means you can simultaneously observe your experience objectively while sensing the associated emotions and sensations (Choosing Therapy, 2022). This is why working on your awareness and mindset before treatment is necessary.

Average cost per Session: $125-$200

Insurance Coverage:
It may be covered under your "therapy" benefits

Average Recommended # of Sessions: 20 or more

Average Time per Session: 45-60 minutes

Typical Preparation for Session: Comfortable clothing

Could be helpful with:

- Trauma

- Trauma-Related Disorders

- Unhealthy attachments

- Many More (Choosing Therapy, 2022)

2. Dance/Movement Therapy

Dance and Movement Therapy is a creative and expressive approach to therapy that uses the language of movement to explore your emotions, enhance mindfulness, and improve your range of motion (Kiepe et al., 2012). This type of therapy is literally dancing your way to recovery, with each step bringing you closer to peace. It is a dance party where your body gets to be the DJ, therapist, and backup dancers all at once! It's a fun and surprisingly effective approach to healing. During sessions, you'll groove, twirl, and shimmy your way through your feelings, letting your body move while your mind catches a breather. Dance interventions also aim to improve your postural and balance control, drawing on the interconnectedness of movement and emotion. This therapy yields psychological and physical benefits across five key areas: resocialization, nonverbal emotional expression, heightened self-awareness and self-esteem, improved muscular coordination and release of tension, and enhanced relaxation and enjoyment (GoodTherapy Editor Team, 2018c).

Engaging in dance therapy activates various parts of the brain, leading to structural changes observed in recent studies. These include increased volume in memory-related regions like the hippocampus and parahippocampal areas, enhanced gray matter volume linked to motor control, and increase white matter integrity in the regions that facilitate communication between your brain hemispheres.

Dance/movement therapists employ techniques such as mirroring to show empathy and validate your experiences. They also incorporate rhythmic movements, especially for those experiencing depression. Additionally, therapists use movement metaphors, props, or gestures to help you symbolize your progress, such as celebrating an emotional surrender with a symbolic white flag. It's even been shown to increase your pain tolerance (Tarr et al., 2015). A session can be private or in a group. It might include guided movement exercises, or you may be encouraged to move freely to express your feelings.

Average Cost per Session: $60-$150

Insurance Coverage:
It may be covered under your "therapy" benefits

Average Recommended # of Sessions:
2-5 sessions per week for 4 to 10 weeks

Average Time per Session: 45-120 minutes

Typical Preparation for Session:
Comfortable clothing to move in

Could be helpful with:

- Depression (Karkou et al., 2019)

- Anxiety

- Parkinson's disease & dementia (Kiepe et al., 2012)

- Neurodivergent

- Eating Disorders

- Trauma

- Fibromyalgia (Kiepe et al., 2012)

- Many more (GoodTherapy Editor Team, 2018c)

3. EMDR (Eye Movement Desensitization & Reprocessing)

EMDR is known to be a profound therapeutic approach that will help with recovery from trauma and is often used to treat PTSD. Through a carefully structured process, EMDR allows you to access and reprocess distressing memories, emotions, and beliefs that have become "stuck" (Boidy, 2023).

By using eye movements, taps, or sounds as bilateral stimulation, EMDR assists in the awareness of traumatic experiences, enabling them to be processed and resolved. EMDR utilizes vibrating devices such as buzzers, pulsers, and tappers held in the user's hands or attached to their wrists. These devices generate intermittent physical sensations, and their timing is utilized to administer stimuli on opposite sides of the body. Typically, the intervals between the vibrations range from 1.5 to 3 seconds. Some therapists use light bars with moving lights to create bilateral stimulation where your eyes track the lights back and forth. This gentle yet powerful method promotes healing at a deep level, leading to a reduction in emotional distress and the emergence of new insights and perspectives (Van Den Hout & Engelhard, 2012).

Your treatment will comprise eight distinct phases

Phase 1: History Taking: In this initial phase, a treatment plan and objectives are identified with discussions about your history, emotional triggers, symptoms, and desired outcomes. The therapist may also consider supplementary therapies alongside EMDR (G. C. Center, 2020).

Phase 2: Preparation: The therapist explains EMDR and addresses any queries. Coping techniques, including stress reduction methods like breathing exercises, are introduced to manage emotions during and between sessions.

Phase 3: Assessing the Target Memory: The focus here is on detecting and analyzing the memory causing emotional distress. Elements such as imagery, thought process, mood, and bodily sensations related to the memory are evaluated to establish a baseline for monitoring progress (Gunter & Bodner, 2008).

Phases 4-7: Treatment (Desensitization, Reaction, Installation, Closure): Phase 4 initiates desensitizing the distressing memory. You would then recall parts of the memory while the therapist guides specific eye movements (Gunter & Bodner, 2008). You would then reflect on the thoughts, feelings, and reactions experienced during the recall. This helps in tracking progress and instilling positive emotional responses and beliefs. If reprocessing is incomplete, a stress-reduction exercise may be conducted before concluding the Session.

Phase 8: Re-evaluation: After each Session, you and the therapist will assess the effects of the treatment, identify uncovered memories, and determine which memories to address in the subsequent session **(Boidy, 2023).**

EMDR offers a path to liberation from the shackles of trauma. You will move through the landscapes of your memory to things you may have forgotten. You will explore the corridors of your mind guided by a skilled navigator.

You may encounter moments of intensity, yet you will always feel protected and encouraged while in treatment. The therapist's gentle guidance will help you navigate the emotional terrain and untangle knots of distress (G. C. Center, 2020). A variety of theories seek to explain the mechanisms of EMDR. According to the working memory hypothesis, EMDR operates on the premise of a competition between the areas in the brain responsible for storing visual and auditory information and the region managing working memory.

Under this theory, retrieving a memory while simultaneously moving your eyes back and forth compels your brain to allocate resources. You cannot focus solely on memory retrieval because you are also engaged with visual stimuli. This divided focus may diminish the clarity of any distressing images you recollect, potentially creating a sense of comfortable detachment from them. Consequently, you might experience the emotional intensity of those memories with less force.

Furthermore, the bilateral stimulation of the brain may induce a heightened state of relaxation. As the recollections become progressively less vivid, your brain may begin to link memory retrieval with a sense of calm rather than emotional distress, ultimately leading to desensitization (Gunter & Bodner, 2008).

Alternative hypotheses regarding the mechanism of EMDR therapy are:

Replication of Rapid Eye Movement (REM) sleep phase:
The oscillation of eye movements back and forth might assist the brain in consolidating memories akin to how it occurs during REM sleep.

Thalamocortical binding:
Eye movements may directly influence the cerebral zone known as the thalamus, potentially triggering a series of cognitive processes that enable better regulation of emotional distress.

Variances in brain structure:
It's conceivable that individuals who exhibit positive responses to EMDR therapy may possess variances in both the form and function of their brain.

Talk with your practitioner before starting treatment if you are diagnosed with bipolar disorder or Personality Disorder.

Average Cost per Session: $150-$200

Insurance Coverage:
Most likely for Post-Traumatic Stress syndrome (Psylaris, 2022)

Average Recommended # of Sessions: 3-12

Average Time per Session: 1 hour to 90 minutes

Typical Preparation for Session:

- Stress-reducing activities like a walk in nature or gentle stretching

- Meditation or breathing exercises for 10 minutes a day

- Complete a daily gratitude journal

- Avoid contact lenses due to dry eyes; glasses are ok (Boidy, 2023)

Could be helpful with:

- PTSD

- Anxiety

- Phobias

- Many More

4. Biofeedback

Biofeedback is excellent for gaining control over your stress response. This method will teach you how to regulate and influence your physiological processes through electronic monitoring devices (Budzynski, 1978). During treatment, you will learn how to rewire your brain by adjusting your response in the moment as various tests pick up on subtle changes.

During biofeedback training, you will go through 3 stages: becoming aware, learning to control responses, and using the skills independently. In the first stage, you'll undergo a psychophysiological stress profile (PSP) developed by Budzynski et al. (1980) to understand how your body responds to stressors. A PSP measures heart rate, muscle tension, and skin conductance. Your breathing, sweat, and even skin temperatures are evaluated. Painless sensors measure your baseline physical responses, followed by controlled stressors and recovery cycles (Professional, n.d.). The controlled stressors can be both cognitive and somatic (Hollie, 2019).

Below are various examples of controlled stressors you could encounter:

Cognitive Challenges: Tasks such as solving math problems, memory recall exercises, or other mental activities that demand focused concentration.

Visual Stimulants: Controlled exposure to stimuli like flashing lights or specific visual patterns is employed to trigger targeted visual processing responses.

Auditory Stimulants: Deliberate exposure to diverse sounds or tones, including sudden loud noises or specific frequencies, can provoke distinct auditory responses.

Breathing Techniques: Purposefully altering breathing patterns, such as adopting slow, deep breaths or rapid, shallow breaths, can influence heart rate and other physiological parameters.

Emotional Visualization: Employing guided visualization techniques, individuals can evoke particular emotional responses, ranging from tranquility to agitation.

Sensory Stimulation: Purposeful application of tactile or sensory stimuli, such as gentle touch or pressure, can elicit specific sensory responses (Professional, n.d.).

After the electrodes or sensors are in place, you may see an image on a computer monitor, hear a beeping sound, or see a flashing light to indicate any changes. You will get to see the results in real time. This helps observe your body's stress reactions and how quickly they return to the baseline. Your results will guide the therapist in customizing your biofeedback training (What to Expect During a Biofeedback Session, n.d.).

Stage two focuses on controlling specific physical responses identified through the PSP. For instance, if muscle tension causes discomfort, you'll learn to relax those muscles (Hollie, 2019).

The final stage is when you attain the ability to make these adjustments without relying on the machine or being tested. You will gain the skills needed to manage physical and emotional issues linked to your stress responses. This could help with headaches, high blood pressure, digestive problems, and overall stress. Additionally, biofeedback training helps build a stronger mind-body connection as you practice emotional regulation and stress reduction techniques. This treatment is not known to have any side effects (Hollie, 2019).

Average cost per Session: **$35-$85**

Insurance Coverage:
It's possible, as some carriers do cover this

Average Recommended # of Sessions: **8-20**

Average Time per Session:
30-60 minutes in addition to homework

Typical Preparation for Session:
List of medications, symptoms, goals, and medical history

Could be helpful with:

- Anxiety

- Depression

- PTSD

- ADHD

- Breathing problems, such as asthma

- Digestive issues, such as irritable bowel syndrome and constipation

- Sleep Disturbances

- Fibromyalgia

- Other Chronic Pain and joint and muscle pain

- Diabetes

- Epilepsy

- High blood pressure

- Addiction

- Many More (Hollie, 2019) (Professional, n.d.)

5. Neurofeedback

Neurofeedback is a category of biofeedback therapy that implements a real-time display of brain activity so you can learn to self-regulate your brainwaves. It promotes improved cognitive functioning and emotional balance. Neurofeedback utilizes an electroencephalogram (EEG), a noninvasive device that gauges brain electrical activity, to teach you how to monitor and regulate your brain functions. The aim is to induce behavioral changes. The interconnectedness of the brain and body means that altering behavior can reciprocally influence brain activity and vice versa (A New Theory of Consciousness: The Mind Exists as a Field Connected to the Brain - SAND, n.d.).

This is could be useful for those recognized to have ADHD, which is characterized by heightened distractibility and diminished concentration, as it offers potential benefits in enhancing focus and attentiveness. Studies indicate that individuals with ADHD exhibit a higher occurrence of sluggish theta waves and a lower occurrence of speedy beta waves. Neurofeedback aims to restore these wave patterns to baseline levels, potentially mitigating ADHD symptoms.

In a neurofeedback session, you'll have an initial assessment, gathering details regarding your symptoms and treatment history. You'll then have a cap with painless electrodes on your head to measure your brain activity. Subsequent sessions involve performing various cognitive tasks while wearing the headgear. These tasks could range from simple activities like listening to a tone to more complex ones like playing a specially designed video game for neurofeedback therapy where your brainwaves are the joystick.

This is serious brain training!

Average cost per Session:
up to $1000 to set up and $125 per session

Insurance Coverage: It's possible, depending on the plan

Average Recommended # of Sessions: 30-40

Average Time per Session: 45-60 minutes

Typical Preparation for Session:

- Be well rested

- Avoid alcohol, nicotine, and cannabis 24 hours before

- Clean/dry hair, avoid hair products

- Eat a small snack 1-3 hours before (How to Prepare for an Optimal Neurofeedback Session, 2023)

It could be helpful with:

- ADD / ADHD

- PTSD

- Neurodivergent

- Depression

- Anxiety

- Stress

- Sleep Disturbances

- Addictions

- Many more

6. Hakomi Therapy

Incorporating mindfulness, somatic intelligence, and non-violence, Hakomi Therapy adopts a body-centered perspective. This supports healing and self-discovery. It combines elements of awareness, touch, and talk therapy to explore how unconscious beliefs and memories are held in the body. It aims for a deeper understanding and release of these patterns (Hakomi Therapy | Therapy Types | Zencare, n.d.). It will examine your gestures, posture, facial expressions, and other body reactions. It focuses on exploring and transforming your unconscious patterns and beliefs by focusing on the body's senses, emotions, and memories. This therapy process is focused on mindfulness (GoodTherapy Editor Team, 2018a).

The therapist could ask questions that may trigger flashbacks, sensations, and feelings. It may include role-playing and guided imagery exercises. A trained professional will promote trust and provide gentle guidance and a safe place for your untold tales to unfold. This therapy gives a voice to your hidden pain. It effectively challenges your self-defeating thoughts and discovers your subconscious thoughts and beliefs.

The Hakomi Method is based on five principles:

Mindfulness (attention inward)

Organicity (the human capacity to heal)

Non-violence (supportive environment)

Mind-body integration (mind-body-spirit as one)

Unity (removing barriers between yourself and others) (Hakomi Therapy | Therapy Types | Zencare, n.d.))

Hakomi sessions follow a structured sequence: contact, accessing, processing, and integration. "Contact" establishes a safe and accepting environment for self-exploration. Without trust and safety, you may resist vulnerability and mindfulness. "Accessing" employs mindfulness to uncover unconscious core material. Unconscious core material refers to your deep-seated beliefs, emotions, and memories that shape your behavior and perceptions, often outside your conscious awareness. The therapist will guide you to explore new options by focusing inward and observing sensations, images, and memories (Hakomi Therapy | Therapy Types | Zencare, n.d.). They will probe your beliefs, often evoking reactions as expressions of your core beliefs. "Processing" involves studying your responses, exploring your principles, and creating new experiences to counteract them. This can lead to significant insight and transformation. "Integration" helps you make sense of your experiences and connect them to life outside therapy (GoodTherapy Editor Team, 2018a).

Hakomi therapy may include consensual touch to support you during emotional moments. It can comfort and encourage you to stay within the experience. Touch is used to support the management of your behaviors, facilitating a deeper exploration (GoodTherapy Editor Team, 2018a). Not all therapists employ touch, and consent is always sought.

Hakomi has shown capability in treating mental health issues like ADHD, anxiety, trauma, and depression. Hakomi principles have been adapted for individual, couple, family, and group therapy (Hakomi Therapy | Therapy Types | Zencare, n.d.).

Average cost per Session:
$80-$300 depending on whether it is an individual, couple, or group session and the length of the session

Insurance Coverage: It is possible for plans that cover "therapy."

Average Recommended # of Sessions: 3-6

Average Time per Session: 50 - 90 minutes

Typical Preparation for Session:
Inform your therapist of your current boundaries and limitations

It could be helpful with:

- Depression

- Stress

- Anxiety

- ADHD

- Trauma

- Sexual Dysfunction

- Relationship concerns

- Many More (GoodTherapy Editor Team, 2018a)

7. Somatic Experiencing® / SE®:

Somatic Experiencing®, created by Dr. Levine, is a therapeutic approach that focuses on resolving trauma and restoring the body's natural ability to self-regulate. By bringing awareness to physical sensations and gradually processing overwhelming experiences, SE can help release your stored trauma and promote healing at a somatic level (GoodTherapy Editor Team, 2018b).

You will be introduced to small amounts of traumatic memories, images, or thoughts. You will report back feelings such as heaviness, tightness, or dizziness. Keep in mind that the therapist will pay close attention to avoid triggering you or causing re-traumatization (Levine, 2010).

You may experience uncomfortable yet familiar feelings running through your body during the process. However, this is exactly what you want as, over time, you will learn to self-regulate these feelings and transform them into comfort more easily. The therapist will guide you to release frozen fragments of trauma and trapped stress, allowing you to regain your body's natural resilience and vitality. This treatment can help you restore balance to your nervous system. With delicate precision, the goal is to allow the body to completely work through the traumatic event (Levine, 2010). This can reduce or eliminate your symptoms. Somatic Experiencing Practitioners® (SEP) come from diverse backgrounds in various approaches and therapies. You will find SEP's® specializing in talk therapy, Psychiatry, Craniosacral, Bodywork, and even Equine Therapy. Somatic Experiencing™ Practitioners may use specialized and trademarked equipment during your session, including Smovey Rings®, which utilize vibrations that align with your body's natural frequencies, offering a calming sensation. The oscillations produced by swinging the rings have demonstrated effectiveness in gaining awareness and managing activated and dissociative states within your nervous system. The Bellicon Rebounder® is a tool that aids in regulation, pendulation, and grounding.

The Tuning Board® is a psychokinesthetic or mind-body device designed to enhance healing through heightened embodiment. It activates the body's natural balance system, boosting your confidence and sense of stability. It was designed to discover latent mind/body patterns associated with trauma. The Bodyblade®, created by Bryce Hymanson, PT, is a vibration and inertia training device that is a valuable tool in trauma healing. It enables you to access more profound emotional experiences by providing sensations of tranquility and contentment in your own body. Engaging your core muscles will aid in the safe processing of intense emotions. It can allow for the release of blocked energies.

Average cost per Session:
$185-$275, depending on if for an individual or couple's session

Insurance Coverage: It is possible for plans that cover "therapy."

Average Recommended # of Sessions:
4-20, based on the intricacies of your case

Average Time per Session: 45-60 minutes

Typical Preparation for a Session:

- Set goals for treatment

- Comfortable clothes

It could be helpful with:

- Trauma

- Trauma-related anxiety, hypervigilance, violence, and shame

- Panic Attacks

- Phobias

- Night terrors

- Addictive behaviors

- Fibromyalgia

- Mood Swings

- Many More (GoodTherapy Editor Team, 2018b)

8. Bioenergetic Analysis

Bioenergetic Analysis is similar to the previously described Sensorimotor Psychotherapy; however, some key differences exist. While Sensorimotor Psychotherapy is more trauma-focused, Bioenergetic Analysis gives attention to all emotions, including trauma, especially those related to childhood experiences.

Bioenergetic therapists are commonly licensed mental health professionals who have extended their expertise through training in bioenergetics principles. Your therapist should create a secure environment where you can freely and truthfully express yourself. During your treatment, you may discuss your life's prenatal, natal, and postnatal periods. This process combines talk therapy with physical exercises and methods to quiet anxiety, grow awareness, and promote inner peace. Treatment could include grounding and movement exercises, as well as breathing techniques (Wisdom, 2023). The goal is to be more open to feeling your feelings like sadness, anger, and fear instead of ignoring or letting them control you. This therapy intends to find a rhythmic connection between your breath and movement. It can revive your body's natural wisdom to dive deep into the sensations that reside within. You will examine your musculature, including the knots of tension and confined stagnant energy (Bioenergetic Analysis (BA) - European Association for Psychotherapy, 2019). Your session might include hitting an object while yelling, stretching, or letting yourself fully cry. This therapy can revitalize your spirit and guide you toward authentic self-expression. It can help you change the way your overall body feels. If comfortable, the therapist may use touch or massage as part of the treatment. (View of a Traumatic Event | Bioenergetic Analysis, n.d.) It may be challenging to locate a formally trained Bioenergetic Analysis practitioner as training takes 4-6 years.

Average cost per Session: **$150-$180**

Insurance Coverage: **It is possible for plans that cover "therapy"**

Average Recommended # of Sessions:
Minimum of 5 plus homework

Average Time per Session: **45-120 minutes**

Typical Preparation for Session:
Ask your family for details about your life's prenatal, natal, and postnatal periods, if possible.

It could be helpful with:

- Anxiety & Depression

- Anger management

- Trauma

- Phobias & Panic Attacks

- OCD & Compulsive Disorders

- Grief

- Chronic Pain

- Addictions

- Many more

9. Polyvagal-Informed Intervention / Nervous System Guided Counseling

Like Sensorimotor Psychotherapy, the Polyvagal-Informed Intervention is a trauma-focused treatment. It refers to therapeutic approaches developed by Stephen Porges that are grounded in the tenets of the polyvagal theory and the proper functioning of the vagus nerve. This theory is based on research on the vagus nerve and its calming effects. The vagus nerve is the most extensive in the body and connects your brain to other organs like the intestines and lungs (Porges, 2003). Chapter 4 has a complete discussion of this theory and the vagus nerve; however, here is a brief rundown. Trauma can significantly affect this nerve's function, leading to dysfunction throughout the body. A dysregulation of the vagus nerve may cause some people to completely shut down their natural response system. This leaves some people with no fight-flight-freeze response while others are constantly "stuck" in this state. Those without a response may feel disconnected or empty inside. At the same time, the latter live in constant high levels of physical pain due to fatigued muscles, among other things. This treatment is less about your thoughts and more about your nervous system's response and restoring regular activity to the nerve. Therapies using this approach aim to regulate the three states of the Autonomic Nervous System to promote a sense of security, connection, and strength (Denver, 2004).

The three states are:

- **The Sympathetic nervous state** - controls the fight-or-flight chemical reactions

- **The Dorsal vagal state** - puts you in a freeze condition like a deer in headlights when danger is perceived

- **The Parasympathetic state** - helps relax your body after stress and danger by slowing your heart and breath rates while lowering your blood pressure

Once activated, the body's fight-flight-freeze chemical reaction can take 20-60 minutes to subside. The treatment goal is to reduce the time between your reaction and returning to a state of calmness. A therapy session may utilize various breathing techniques as you discuss your trauma. You may also use vocalizations like humming, singing, or chanting to directly stimulate your vagus nerve. You could also use sound healing that utilizes sonic vibrations to balance the nervous system and aid emotional release. You may also talk about happy memories that would release oxytocin. Your therapist may also include playful exercises, meditation, or aromatherapy.

There is a specialized Polyvagal-informed intervention called Safe and Sound protocol® or SSP®. Specially trained practitioners may use SSP® developed by Dr. Stephen Porges. The SSP® treatment will use audible cues to reduce emotional reactivity and stress. Emotional reactivity means how easily and intensely you express emotions. A highly reactive person responds vigorously and quickly, while a low-level reactive person responds less quickly and powerfully. SSP® treatment could be as easy as listening to specially modified music on your home computer. The music is designed to exercise your inner ear, sending signals through your nervous system. It's known for having quite a calming effect (Geek, 2023). A typical treatment could be listening for 1 hour a day for 5 days. However, some only listen to this for 1 to 15 minutes at a time, as this can be a powerful and overwhelming treatment. Be sure to report all reactions to your therapist.

Average cost per Session: $150-$225; **SSP** $500-$1000

Insurance Coverage:
It is possible for plans that cover "therapy"; however, insurance will not cover the SSP treatment

Average Recommended # of Session: **Varies**

Average Time per Session: **45-60 minutes**

Typical Preparation for Session:
For safe and sound protocol (SSP), avoid electronic devices while listening; you may do a puzzle or art while in session

It could be helpful with:

- Fibromyalgia & Other chronic pain

- PTSD

- ADHD

- Trauma

- Sensory processing difficulties

- Chronic fatigue

- Anxiety

- Depression

- Phobias

- Sleep disturbance

- Many more

10. Body-Mind Centering® / BMC®

Body-Mind Centering® is a blend of Western medicine and Eastern philosophies, developed and registered by Bonnie Bainbridge Cohen. It focuses on studying anatomy and physiology and their connection to consciousness. BMC® involves hands-on techniques, movement exercises, and guided imagery to explore the body's tissues, organs, and systems relating to emotional and psychological experiences.

Your skeleton, ligaments, muscles, organs, tissues, glands, fluids, fat, and skin are acknowledged as having a voice. The purpose is to align your inner cellular awareness with your outer awareness and movements. It emphasizes experiential learning and uses touch, movement, and imagery. You could use this to access and deepen your understanding of your body's systems, patterns, and developmental processes. In a BMC® session, the practitioner may encourage an exploration of your body's physical and energetic aspects. You may use spinal movements, breathing exercises, and vocalization techniques.

Throughout the session, you will be prompted to bring awareness to your bodily sensations, explore different movement patterns, and engage in specific exercises designed to target particular networks in your body all the way down to the cellular level. The therapy space may resemble an exercise room with mats, balls, and other tools. You will discover new ways of moving, releasing trauma, and feeling whole again. BMC® practitioners are highly specialized, completing over 2000 hours of training.

Average cost per Session: $60-$150

Insurance Coverage: It is possible for plans that cover "therapy"

Average Recommended # of Sessions: Varies by case

Average Time per Session: 60-90 minutes

Typical Preparation for Session: Dress comfortably

It could be helpful with:

- Trauma

- Stress

- Anxiety

- Many more

11. Trauma-informed Yoga

Trauma-informed yoga is a mindful and compassionate approach to yoga that recognizes and respects the impacts of trauma. For some people, common yoga classes or poses can be emotionally unsettling. Trauma-informed yoga attempts to address these concerns by creating a safe environment to give a voice to your emotions instead of keeping them bottled up. It can help you regain a sense of control and ownership over your body. In a typical session, the workspace is arranged with consideration toward security and assurance. For example, generally, you wouldn't be in a position with your back toward the door. The space should be well-lit, and the experience should make you feel welcome (Rice, 2022).

As you know, trauma can strip away a person's autonomy and choice. This therapy will strengthen you with full control over your experience. It is understood that you can use as much time on whatever movements you'd like to explore. Keep in mind there is no physical touch during instruction, which will differ from a typical yoga class. If you've never tried yoga, there is no need to worry. Trauma-informed yoga is excellent for all skill levels, including primarily gentle poses and focused breathing. It's a journey where your body and mind harmonize, creating strength and self-compassion (West et al., 2017).

Average cost per Session:

- $60-$100 private session

- $15-$30 group session

Insurance Coverage:
Depends - possible if referred for rehabilitation, yes, for some Veterans, or if your therapist is Trauma-Informed Yoga certified and can bill under "therapy"

Average Recommended # of Sessions: **4-10**

Average Time per Session: **60 minutes**

Typical Preparation for Session:

- Wear comfortable clothing

- May need a yoga mat

It could be helpful with:

- Trauma

- Sexual Assault survivors

- PTSD

- Depression

- Stress

- Anxiety

- Self-esteem and confidence concerns

- Anger

- Dissociation

- Many more (Rice, 2022)

12. Feldenkrais Method®

The Feldenkrais Method®, developed and registered by Dr. Moshe Feldenkrais, is great for those living with chronic pain and mobility issues. It is an educational approach to increase maneuverability and performance by improving self-awareness and exploring gentle, mindful motion. It's similar to traditional physical therapy, focusing on improving sensorimotor function and boosting the mind-body connection. The Feldenkrais Method® uses the brain's neuroplasticity – the ability to learn and adapt to create new yet natural ways of moving. This can help reduce how much chronic pain affects your daily life. This method does not seek to treat the cause of your pain but rather to help you master techniques to address it in a new and effective way. The gentle movements spark the brain to rewire so that your old movements are no longer in the way. This method uses subtle motions and concentrated awareness to enhance your mobility, flexibility, coordination, and overall performance in both physical and mental tasks (Admin_Feldenkrais, n.d.).

You could have guided group classes or personalized private lessons. Sessions consist of gentle movements followed by rest periods, promoting deep relaxation and effective learning. A typical session may involve lying or sitting on a low padded table. The practitioner will discover your current habits and movements using precise touch and sometimes verbal instructions to offer you new and better options.

Private lessons are highly customized to your needs and patterns of movement. Sessions typically last 45 minutes to an hour, and workshops with themed lessons over several hours or days are often available for further exploration and learning.

A Certified FGNA Practitioner is highly specialized, having at least 800 hours of training over 3 years.

Average cost per Session:

- $100-$150 Private session

- $15-$30 Group session

Insurance Coverage:
possible if billed under "therapy" or even "physical therapy"

Average Recommended # of Sessions: 4 or more

Average Time per Session: 30-60 minutes

Typical Preparation for Session: Comfortable, loose clothing

It could be helpful with:

- Chronic pain

- Fibromyalgia

- Muscle and joint pain

- Sleep concerns

- Balance concerns

- Neurodivergent

- Many more

13. Art Therapy

This method will provide a safe and non-verbal means of dialogue, allowing you to explore through various artistic mediums. The term "art therapy" could refer to visual art, music, drama, or dance techniques (What Are Arts and Creative Therapies?, n.d.). However, participating in any of these allows you to express your thoughts and emotions, with or without talking (Gitnux, 2023). This can provide excellent symptom relief for those not quite ready to discuss the trauma or those seeking another way to communicate (Admin & Admin, 2023). For example, creating an art piece will help you express things that you otherwise can't or won't say with words. Many expressions from your subconscious mind could come forward during a therapy session. The goal is to gain previously unknown insights into your actions, thoughts, and emotions. This therapeutic approach uses the creative process to promote a balanced mood and improve your coping skills and mental focus (Hamel, 2021). Depending on what sparks your passion, this may include drawing, painting, performing, dancing, or singing. Art Therapy is a magical tool that will help you reveal yourself through creativity. Creativity is what connects you to your intuition. You will extract your emotions and story as you design and communicate without words.

This therapy is for **everyone**; no experience, skills, or training is needed to participate.

Creating or experiencing art will boost your brain function by influencing your brain wave patterns, emotions, and nervous system (Gitnux, 2023). It is important for your mood and sleep patterns as it can also raise your serotonin levels (Admin & Admin, 2023). You may be asked questions before, during, or after the experience. However, you can choose to create in silence if that's your preference. Your creation will be a safe space where chaos and pain can find comfort and release. Art will connect your conscious and subconscious minds, leading you towards self-awareness and feeling complete.

Average cost per Session:

- $75-$175 Private session

- $10-$50 Group session

Insurance Coverage:
Possible, if billed under "therapy" or with a referral of medical necessity

Average Recommended # of Sessions: 8 to 15

Average Time per Session: **45-90 minutes**

Typical Preparation for Session:
Think about what materials you'd like to work with

It could be helpful with:

- Anxiety

- Depression

- Stress

- Trauma

- Bi-Polar Disorder

- Neurodivergent

- Chronic Pain

- PTSD

- Grief

- Dementia

- Many more (Hamel, 2021)

14. Breathwork

This is one of my favorites, with roots in yoga; breathwork is one of the most primal and oldest known practices, dating back thousands of years. These techniques aim for purposeful command and strategic breath manipulation to boost your holistic well-being (Ashton, 2022).

It is also known as intentional breath control. Using specific breathing techniques, breathwork aims to release tension and increase energy, self-awareness, and healing. Through this practice you will gain self-awareness that contributes to releasing stored body trauma. Breathwork exercises can provide immediate relief, as taking control of your breath enables you to pause and guide the path of your emotional current (Zaccaro et al., 2018). A typical breathwork session is conducted by a certified practitioner. For example, you could be directed to practice rapid-paced breathing for a specific period. These exercises are done lying down as you may go into other states of consciousness. See Chapter 4 to learn about the different states of consciousness. Chapter 5 is dedicated to breathwork; this time-tested, powerful practice will give you all the details needed to start your new life.

Average cost per Session:

- $125-$200 private or couple's Session

- $20-$50 group session

Insurance Coverage: No, in most cases

Average Recommended # of Sessions:
1-20 plus regular homework

Average Time per Session: **20-60 minutes**

Typical Preparation for a Session:

- May need a yoga mat

- Avoid eating an hour before the session

It could be helpful with:

- Stress

- PTSD

- Anxiety

- Fibromyalgia

- Other Chronic Pain

- Releasing toxins

- Many more - see Chapter 5

15. Authentic Movement®

Authentic Movement®, developed by Mary Starks Whitehouse, is a form of art therapy focusing on dance and movement. There are no directions to follow; you are entirely self-directed. It is a meditative practice where you will learn to listen to cues from your body to guide the movement. You will have your eyes closed to reduce distractions. It is a practice that involves deep listening to your body's impulses, allowing unprompted and genuine movement to present itself.

The focus is on expressing spontaneous movements; some therapists include music, while others do not (GoodTherapy Editor Team, 2016). Feel free to vocalize, dance, stay still, or experiment with different forms of conveying emotions if inspired.

This practice is distinct because there are roles to play. At all times, there is a mover and a witness. The witness's role is to provide emotional balance and safety. The witness will share with you their observations to help you reflect. They will ensure you feel seen and heard. You may switch roles from mover to witness during your session (GoodTherapy Editor Team, 2016). This is great for those who may not be ready to talk about all of their history or trauma yet.

Authentic Movement® offers a unique way to explore who you are. A typical session should be in a peaceful studio, and feel like you're talking to your soul through movement alone. Guided by your breath and intuition, your body will tell untold stories through silent motions. The goal is to discover the vulnerable and the strong parts of yourself (GoodTherapy Editor Team, 2016).

Average cost per Session:

- $100-$180 Private session

- $20-$50 Group session

Insurance Coverage:
It may be covered under your "therapy" benefits

Average Recommended # of Sessions: **7-20**

Average Time per Session: **45-60 minutes**

Typical Preparation for Session:

- Comfortable clothing

- Notepad for reflections

- It could be helpful with:

- Anxiety

- Depression

- Trauma

- ADHD

- And more

Benefits and Constraints of Somatic Therapy

Somatic Therapy offers numerous benefits if you are seeking renewal and self-understanding. It's been beneficial for myself and those close to me. Besides my account, numerous unbiased scientific studies on the subject are accessible for anyone to examine. These methods are scientifically proven and evidence-based (Bloch-Atefi & Ja, 2015).

The benefits of Somatic Therapy could include:

- Reduced physical and psychological discomfort

- Decreased muscle strain and pain

- Decreased stress

- Fewer "bad mood" days

- Minimized irritability or aggressiveness

- Enhanced focus

- Elevated self-awareness

- More "good mood" days

- Improved confidence

- Increased hope

- Increased resiliency

- Increased strength and energy

- Improved relationships

- Improved sleep

- Restored interest in activities

Potential limitations and considerations

While Somatic Therapy has already been proven and has an even more promising future in addressing trauma and stress. It is important to learn the potential drawbacks and considerations.

Somatic Therapy may not be appropriate for everyone, especially those with severe physical restrictions or specific medical conditions. This includes those who may have difficulty fully participating in practices focused on embodiment. Additionally, the effectiveness of Somatic Therapy can vary, and it may require time and consistency for desired outcomes to be achieved. You must approach Somatic Therapy with an open mind and willingness to fully explore the mind-body connection with your chosen techniques. Somatic Therapy isn't a rapid solution and may need sustained support and integration with other therapeutic techniques for complete healing. Finally, it's worth noting that some sessions may come with a significant cost. If cost poses a challenge, some therapists may consider a sliding scale arrangement. Make sure to ask when making your first appointment if they offer any flexible or income-based pricing. You may have minimal options for in-person treatment if you live in a small town. However, certain types of therapy can utilize telehealth or online options. Online sessions are just as effective as in person (Andersson et al., 2014).

Pinpointing the ideal therapist is a unique journey, as finding someone who aligns with your personality, needs, and goals could demand a bit of time. Trust your instincts and take the time to find a therapist who is experienced, empathetic, and supportive.

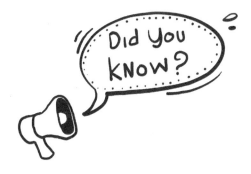

Prolonged stress and burnout may result in a significant disconnect between the body and mind. As per the American Institute of Stress, an astonishing 77% of Americans often experience physical symptoms originating from stress. Issues like headaches, muscle stiffness, and stomach-related problems contribute to a harmful cycle that can further exacerbate the sense of disconnection.

Chapter 3:
Develop a Mindful Presence in the Body First

What to expect in this chapter:

Self-Regulation
Self-Reflection Body Awareness
Proprioception and Interoception
Present-Moment Awareness
Self-Care
Sensory Awareness

You are a garden!

We, as humans, are part of nature. The essence of our lives is the propensity for growth. Imagine your body is like a secret garden, lush and vibrant, with the potential for growth and transformation. However, over time, life's challenges, traumas, and stressors create a thick layer of overgrowth that hides your garden's true beauty and inhibits your vitality.

If left unaddressed, stress is just like plant rot; it can quietly infiltrate your life, eroding your well-being from within. Somatic Therapy is the key that unlocks your garden's gate, allowing you to step inside and tend to the neglected areas. The therapist acts as a skilled gardener, guiding you as you navigate the overgrown pathways and tangled greenery. You will work with your therapist, and your task is to clear away the accumulated debris of past wounds, pruning back the thorny bushes of pain and unraveling the invasive vines of tension. With each session, you will nurture the soil of your body, allowing the seeds of healing to take root. While cultivating your garden, you will discover hidden gems like the sparkling ponds of self-awareness, the colorful blossoms of emotional release, and the fragrant herbs of self-compassion that were planted.

With each session, your garden begins to flourish again.

The once-barren areas will become lush with strength and a renewed sense of wholeness.

Somatic Therapy activates your power to cultivate a deep connection with your body, tending to the hidden garden within you. Through this journey, you will learn to nurture yourself, embracing the beauty beneath the surface. It's all about tending to your emotions. Self-regulation and self-reflection are your natural fertilizers.

Think of body awareness as the mulch that nurtures your growth. In contrast, present-moment awareness serves as a shovel, helping you dig deep into the soil of self-discovery. Consider self-care as the life-sustaining water that quenches your inner thirst. At the same time, sensory awareness acts as the framework, guiding your personal growth and supporting your healing journey. These things are required to nurture the most beautiful garden within you. These are the ingredients of peace.

"You have power over your mind – not outside events. Realize this, and you will find strength."

— Marcus Aurelius   (Marcus Aurelius Quotes. (n.d.)

We must self-regulate!

Emotional regulation, aka self-regulation, is the talent of noticing, processing, and mastering your emotions. With practice, you can adapt to the constantly shifting dynamics of your feelings. Mastering this ability doesn't mean you will never have a negative emotion or struggle; it simply means knowing how to move past them more effectively. It includes remaining calm in stressful situations and coping with negative emotions like anger or anxiety while maintaining a positive outlook. When life changes, we have to face a new reality. It's not easy, but accepting your new reality is the only good option.

Keep in mind that not all anger is destructive. It's natural for everyone to feel the emotion of anger and shouldn't always be seen as negative. It can be helpful as a signal that something is wrong, motivating us to address issues and set boundaries. Anger can also act as mental armor, protecting us from potential threats. However, uncontrolled anger can cause significant damage to yourself and everything around you. Anyone can successfully control their emotions, behaviors, and impulses with practice. Practicing emotional regulation will help you react to your own internal thoughts and things in your external environment. Part of healing with emotional regulation is admitting that you may not always exhibit traits and behaviors that align with your self-perception. For instance, if you become upset when labeled as impatient, but lately, you might indeed be demonstrating impatience. To effectively regulate yourself, it's essential to recognize and acknowledge your increased impatience. Anger can be a positive force for change when appropriately managed.

Constructive anger promotes assertiveness, establishes clear communication, and strengthens relationships by enforcing boundaries. Without control of this skill, you will struggle to make good decisions for yourself and have trouble reaching your Somatic Therapy (or other) goals. Worst of all, all your relationships will suffer. Improving your emotional self-regulation is foundationally vital to success in life. There are many strategies and techniques that you can use to develop this skill.

When managed constructively, anger can bring us positive change, promote assertiveness, and strengthen relationships by helping you have better communication and boundaries.

Boost your self-regulation by focusing on the following key skills or practices in your daily life activities.

Impulse Control:

Resistance isn't futile. Resisting impulsive behaviors and temptations is crucial. This means delaying gratification and making choices based on long-term goals rather than your immediate desires. One of the greatest gifts you can give yourself is - self-control. For example, someone who uses TV or movies to distract from the pain and trauma instead of starting a healing journey. The art of impulse control can turn your emotions into a valuable instrument for self-reflection and personal development. By pausing before reacting, you can learn to respond thoughtfully and with understanding in every interaction.

Attention Control:

Managing your focus and attention is vital. This involves how you concentrate on tasks, avoid distractions, and your ability to shift your attention when necessary.

For example, someone with good attention control will create a written plan like smart goals to track the progress of their new mindfulness routine. They will set up a quiet environment, turn the phone off during the routine, and actively engage in positive self-talk.

By learning the power of attention control, you can tame the flames of emotion and redirect its focus towards patience.

Behavioral Control:

This is your capacity to regulate your actions and behaviors in a socially acceptable and goal-oriented manner. It involves sticking to your personal standards and values even when emotionally stimulated.

For example, someone lacking behavioral control might lash out by yelling, physically hitting objects, or throwing things when in distress.

Learning the power of behavior control will transform your emotions into a guiding force for positive change. You will gain understanding even during conflict by choosing compassion over your impulses.

Cognitive Control:

This aspect relates to managing and directing your thoughts and mental processes. This involves challenging and changing your unhealthy or illogical thoughts by questioning their validity. It means you can recognize when a self-limiting belief, like those described in Chapter 1, has crept into your mind.

For example, someone who shies away from a dance therapy session because someone else said they "can't dance." Even though this thought is subject to opinion and has no validity on your treatment, lack of cognitive control directed their decision.

Another example is someone practicing mindfulness, and their mind wanders off to thinking about a work deadline or relationship issue.

This skill involves your ability to refocus your thoughts and redirect them back to the present. With better cognitive control, you can transform emotions into wisdom. Reframing thoughts and perspectives allows you to navigate challenges, even in the face of anger.

Stress Management:

Coping with your stress and anxiety in healthy ways is critical to self-regulation. This may involve awareness and movement techniques, breathwork, and mindfulness exercises (Bloch-Atefi & Ja, 2015). It is much harder for you to navigate life and manage your emotions when you are dealing with tension headaches, stiff muscles, and digestive issues. Stress management will help break up any tension and bring you closer to understanding.

Cognitive Restructuring:

Confront and reshape harmful or irrational thoughts that fuel intense emotional responses. Substitute them with more logical and positive variations.

You need to determine if the thought is based on facts and evidence, if your thinking is too "black and white" or "stubborn," or if you may have personalized it.

For example, if a person with a history of trauma experiences a rapid heartbeat during a therapy session, they may have a thought like, "I'm in danger.", activating the fight-flight-freeze response.

You can reframe this thought through cognitive restructuring to something like, "My body is responding to a memory, but I am safe in this present moment." By reshaping negative thoughts, anger has finally met its match.

Emotional Regulation Worksheets:

Many worksheets and workbooks provide exercises and strategies for emotional self-regulation. These can aid and support you as you explore emotions and develop coping skills. Emotional Regulation Worksheets are available in the companion book, "The Blessing: Workbook and Journal of Life with Gratitude" by Naty H.E.A.L.S. These can provide helpful guidance and insights into your self-awareness and healing.

Visualization:

A quick way to help yourself when you experience an intense emotion building is to just stop and imagine a serene and comfortable environment in your mind.

A sanctury just for you.

Visualization can help you immediately shift your focus away from your distressing emotions and help you self-regulate. By imagining landscapes of serenity, you can unlock the power to calm down and find clarity.

Counting:

This is a simple yet mighty tool for when you sense a powerful emotion arising, simply pause and count to ten. This will give you time before you react emotionally.

Counting is a grounding tool that will sync you to tempo of each breath and heartbeat. Counting can diffuse anger and provide time for clarity. This brief pause can help you gain control and to respond thoughtfully.

Use Affirmations:

When you sense a powerful emotion rising, take a moment to pause and recite a positive affirmation to yourself. You can use this moment to say, "I am safe, I am loved, I am protected. " This can be a helpful technique in changing your perspective and handling your emotions. For instance, you might use sentences such as "I am at ease" or "I am skilled" until you feel a sense of calm or confidence. Some other helpful variations include "I feel," "I do," "I love," "I speak," "I see," and "I understand" statements. Affirmations become a soothing balm for your emotions

You are replacing the negative emotions with self-assurance, self-love, and understanding.

Emotional Regulation Apps:

During a flare-up or needing a moment of peace, it's tempting to turn to social media for a instant distraction. Unfortunately, these sources don't offer genuine relief. However, various mobile apps are designed to assist with emotional regulation and mindfulness. These apps provide guided exercises and techniques and can be accessed by anyone with mobile phone service, all while comfortable at home.

> "Reflect upon your present blessings of which every man has many - not on your past misfortunes, of which all men have some"
> – Charles Dickens   (Charles Dickens Quotes. n.d.)

A healing dose of honest self-understanding

In Somatic Therapy, another key factor to consider is self-understanding, aka self-reflection. This is truly knowing who you are including your deepest desires. This is understanding how and why you have developed certain behavioral patterns.

Self-reflection is a conscious examination of the ponderings within your mind, emotions, experiences, and behaviors. It means that you are taking the time to pause and purposefully think about yourself. Working on this talent will clarify your perception of self, what you really believe in, and your relationship with the world

Better self-reflection involves asking yourself questions and contemplating your own thoughts and behaviors. This is the way to gain insights into your values, strengths, weaknesses, motivations, and goals you may only sometimes think about. It can also help you recognize your behavior patterns and pinpoint places that need growth or improvement. This will lead to you making better and more informed life choices.

As humans, some of the most challenging tasks we undertake involve facing ourselves, uttering the truth, etablishing limits, and accepting change. Many people spend their lives running from this and instead turn to sex, drugs, relationships, or anything else that will help them avoid this task. Through self-reflection, you establish room for truthful evaluation and self-awareness. You can practice this skill with powerful tools like journaling and body mapping.

Journaling will allow you to express thoughts, emotions, and experiences privately and introspectively. Writing can help validate your feelings, identify triggers, and help you discover precious insights.

If you need help starting a journal entry, answer this question.
Which one of these emotions are you feeling now?
Pick one or two and start writing.

ACCEPTED

REJECTED

DENIED

IMPATIENT

INDECISIVE

SEARCHING

MOODY

DELIGHTED

CAUTION

FOCUS

FREEZE

HORNY

LIKE

UNLIKE

INFLUENCE

Put it on paper - Body mapping:

Body mapping is the process of creating a visual representation or drawing of your body to explore and identify sensations, emotions, or experiences related to various body parts.

During this exercise, you will trace or draw an outline of your body on paper or use the premade template available in the companion guide. You will create a visible and tangible representation to document the bond between your physical and emotional experiences. Mark or fill in specific areas of the body to denote different sensations or emotions you're presently going through or have felt before. This can include physical sensations like pain, tension, or pleasure and emotional experiences such as joy, sadness, or anxiety. It can provide a record of how your emotions manifest in specific areas of your body.

Body mapping templates are available in the companion book, "The Blessing: Workbook and Journal of Life with Gratitude" by Naty H.E.A.L.S.

Example of my body map:

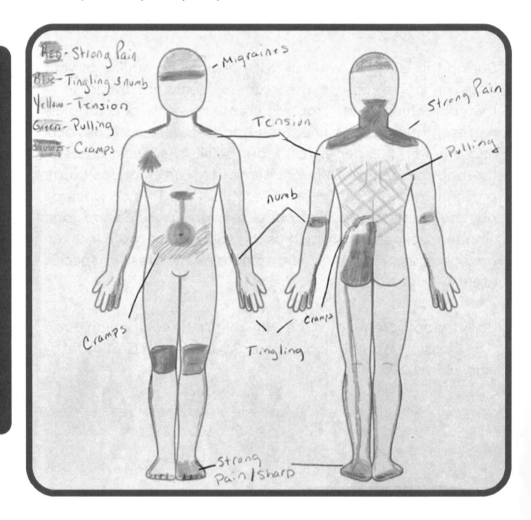

Somatic Therapy is all about proprioception and interoception

If you have never heard these terms before, you are not alone. However, learning basic knowledge of proprioception and interoception will benefit you. They refer to your "gut feelings" about your body's movement and internal sensations. Proprioception is the body's capacity to detect its position, motion, and spatial alignment. It requires integrating sensory information from muscles, tendons, and joints to give the feeling of body awareness and coordination. Proprioception allows you to perform precise motions, sustain equilibrium and move around in life without relying solely on visual cues.

Interoception, on the other hand, relates to the perception and awareness of your internal bodily sensations. It involves sensing and interpreting signals from organs, muscles, and somatic processes such as heartbeat, breathing, hunger, thirst, and emotional states. Interoception is crucial in regulating bodily functions, emotional experiences, and self-awareness. It helps you understand and respond to your internal states and guides your actions and decisions about your physical health and emotional balance.

Techniques to enhance proprioception and interoception involve mindful movement and body awareness, like yoga and Tai Chi. You can also try the mindfulness exercises discussed in the upcoming section on living in the present moment or explore any regimen focusing on deliberate bodily motions. These exercises will help you tune into the intricate feedback from your muscles, joints, and internal organs so you can learn your body's capabilities, limitations, and subtle signals. Regularly practicing these techniques will significantly refine your present-moment awareness, and your proprioception and interoception abilities will definitely increase.

"Do not dwell in the past, do not dream of the future, concentrate the mind on the present moment.."

— Buddha (Buddha Quotes. n.d.)

"If you are depressed you are living in the past.
If you are anxious you are living in the future.
If you are at peace you are living in the present."
— Lao Tzu   (A Quote by Lao Tzu, n.d.)

The present moment!

The only place worth being is right here right now!

The now is where everything happens.

Yesterday is done, and tomorrow is unseen.

Understanding and practicing present-moment awareness involves immersing yourself fully within the current unfolding experience. It is a deliberate act of focusing attention on the here and now, promoting a deep connection with the present. Anything you concentrate on has the tendency to grow stronger in your awareness by rewiring the brain (Marlock et al., 2015, p. 402). Present-moment awareness involves winning the fight between the mind's tendency to ruminate on the past or daydream about the future. I've wasted many years either upset about the past or stressing about the times to come. I often missed out on enjoying my life while it was happening. I allowed my past to control my present moment and all the times ahead, which affected my body, mind, and soul.

Present-moment awareness invites you to fully engage with your feelings, experiences, and mood without critique or holding on to them. Just being there to recognize or experience the sensation, thought, or feeling, not worrying about what to do with them. This practice will cultivate a heightened sense of clarity, insight, and appreciation for the subtle nuances of your existence. Setting up a daily mindfulness practice should be your first step in building your present-moment awareness.

You will learn to enjoy the richness of each passing moment by finding comfort and far-reaching meaning within your own life.

This was such a critical step for me.

A mindfulness practice can be meditation, journaling, or gentle stretching.

Any of these can cultivate a sense of present-moment awareness.

Repeat daily.

To create a mindfulness ritual, start by choosing a specific time and place dedicated to your practice. Settle into a comfortable position, zero in on your breath, and drop all distractions.

Please mute any devices and place them out of view.

Some other mindfulness practices you can apply daily include body scanning and mindful walking.

Body scan meditation:

This involves a gentle and systematic exploration of the body's sensations. Through deliberate focus, you have the opportunity to methodically examine every area, starting from the top and moving down to the toes, acknowledging any tensions, discomfort, or areas of ease

Let's try. Identify a peaceful and secure spot for sitting or lying down. Begin by bringing awareness to your breath, gently inhaling and exhaling, letting the breath serve as your grounding to the current moment. Shut your eyes and engage in a few deep breaths for self-centering.

Rest your hand on the place where your breathing is most evident. This could be your chest or belly; your hand will help you focus on one point.

Then, shift your attention to the remaining parts of your body, starting from the top of your head and progressing downward.

Note any sensations, tension, or areas of discomfort.

With each breath, and as you notice these areas, imagine sending a wave of relaxation and warmth right there.

Visualize the tension melting away or being released with each breath.

Connect with your breath by observing its natural rhythm. Direct your attention to the feeling of your breath flowing in and out.

Gradually scan through the entire body, acknowledging and releasing any sensations that arise. Continue to breathe deeply and consciously, allowing your body to relax further with each exhale. Stay present with the sensations in your body. Take your time to complete the body scan, ensuring you give attention to each body part. When you're ready, gently open your eyes and spend a few moments in reflection on the exercise, considering any insights or emotions that may have come to light.

If you have a partner, you can try biofeedback devices such as a heart rate monitor to observe any changes as you relax. However, this is not required. Regular body scan meditation can become a safe haven for your mind and an excellent tool for creating a gentle awareness.

Mindful walking:

Walking is a natural remedy for your whole body. With every stride, stress can melt away, and clarity can emerge. Instead of rushing through your walks, practice mindful walking.

The intention is to fully observe all details that might normally go unnoticed. When strolling in nature, be mindful of the sensations with each step. Feel the earth under your feet, the motion of your legs, and the cadence of your steps. Describe the feelings in your toes connecting with the ground and the other stimuli around you. Take note of the soundscape, scents, and images without distraction or allowing your mind to drift elsewhere

Feel the sun's warmth on your body, hear to the slight crunch of the dirt, and concentrate on the scents of nearby flowers and trees. Focus on the colors and textures of the natural surroundings. Engaging your senses in this way will give you a sense of calm and centeredness. We all come from nature, so it's natural to feel the earth's energy and peace when outdoors. Focus on your breathing. This type of walking gives you a literal and figurative way to "move on" from distress.

Enhance your sensory awareness and perception

Now that you have learned about living in the present moment, you understand that physical sensations can signal your emotional state. To find balance in life, pay attention to the cues your body gives with different emotions. Sensory awareness and perception involve identifying subtle shifts, such as a quicker heartbeat, shallow breaths, tense muscles, or a tightening in the stomach. These physical cues can serve as valuable indicators, guiding you toward a more profound acknowledgment of your emotional experiences.

"I count him braver who overcomes his desires than him who conquers his enemies; for the hardest victory is over self"- Aristotle   Aristotle Quotes. (n.d.)

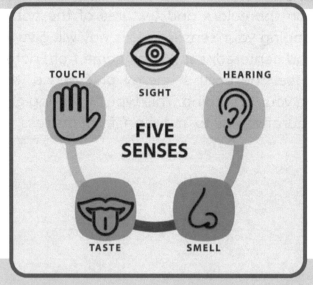

Try the sensory exploration exercises below to enhance your sensory awareness and perception.

These are great exercises to prepare yourself before starting therapy or practicing awareness between sessions. The purpose of these exercises is to actively and attentively involve your senses.

Texture Discovery:

Find objects with various tactile qualities around you, such as a cushiony fabric, a rough stone, a smooth glass surface, or bumpy tree bark. Take a few minutes to explore each object with your hands, paying attention to the unique sensations and textures. Notice how they feel against your skin, temperature, and other tactile qualities.

Sound Immersion:

Sit or lay down in a safe location and shut your eyes. Focus your attention on the sounds around you. Pay attention to the far-off sounds, those nearby, and even the internal ones, like your own breath or heartbeat. Allow the sounds to come and go without getting stuck with them. Simply observe and listen.

I also enjoy listening to indigenous meditation music, Lori beats, Solfeggio frequencies, and rainforest sleep sounds.

Aromatic Journey:

Collect a variety of good smelling things, such as plant-based oil extracts, botanicals, or flora. Shut your eyes and smell each one. Inhale deeply and focus on the aroma. Notice any memories, emotions, or physical sensations that come up as you smell each scent.

Take your time with each one and appreciate its unique fragrance. I suggest that you carry an essential oil nasal inhaler with you. It enhances your sensory awareness and provides a wonderful way to soothe your system when you need it most (Deubner, 2022). Take some time to study the properties of your selected oil and use it as instructed.

Visual Observation:

Choose an object or a natural scene to observe. Look at it closely and attentively, focusing on the colors, shapes, patterns, and details.

Notice the interplay of light and shadow.

Take your time to explore the visual qualities of the object or scene as if witnessing it for the very first time.

Barefoot Walking:

This is a great grounding practice. Find a safe and comfortable area to walk without socks or shoes. Tune into the sensations in your feet as you stroll. Notice the texture, temperature, and varying surfaces as you go.Bring focus to the link between your feet and the ground; with each step, you will also absorb nature's energy.

Taste Testing:

Gather foods or beverages with various tastes, such as sweet, sour, bitter, or salty. Before eating it, observe its texture, color, and shape for a few moments. Notice any aromas it emits. Take slow bites or small sips of each one and notice the flavors, textures, and any changes that occur as you consume each item. Pay attention to the sensations in your mouth and the experience of chewing and swallowing.

Kinetic Movement:

Engage in a physical activity that involves rhythmic and repetitive movements, such as dancing, yoga, or Tai Chi. Be aware of the bodily sensations as you go through the motions, noticing the muscle's stretch, contraction, or flow. Be present with the movement and the physical sensations it generates.

Mindful Shower or Bath:

Instead of taking your shower or bath as usual, focus on this sensory experience. Focus on the sensation of water against your skin. Observe its temperature, and touch and movement. Be present with the sounds the water makes and the scent of any products you use. Fully immerse yourself in the experience without distraction.

Adding Epsom salt, essential oils appropriate for bathing, and candles can help light up your senses. You should take this time to close your eyes and just give yourself a big hug. Hold as tight as you can and enjoy the self-love.

Any of these exercises will help enhance your present-moment awareness practice. However, you should also add a daily self-care ritual to reduce anxiety and depression, lessen stress, and increase your happiness.

> "There are three things extremely hard: steel, a diamond, and to know one's self."
>
> — Benjamin Franklin
>
> Benjamin Franklin Quotes. (n.d.).

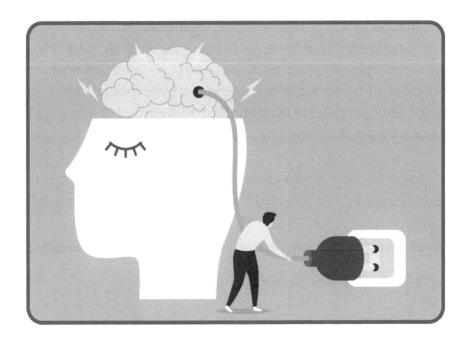

Self-care time!

Self-care is essential for your survival. It entails doing things for yourself to better your whole-body wellness. Starting Somatic Therapy is a huge step for your self-care. Creating a nourishing self-care routine involves intentionally dedicating time and energy to prioritize and nurture yourself. It is a purposeful act of self-love and protection; it's seeing the value of holistically caring for yourself. Self-care isn't a luxury; it's therapy in action. Nurturing your mind, body, and soul is a healing ritual that grants you the strength to handle life's challenges with flexibility and poise. Your routine can include various activities such as exercise, proper nutrition, exploring hobbies, social connections, and defining personal boundaries. This gives the fuel necessary to power your healing.

By committing to a replenishing self-care routine, you will develop a sense of balance, recharge your energy, and cherish a positive relationship with yourself. It is a personalized practice that honors the uniqueness of your exact needs; it is vital for your long-term wholeness and well-being, which is the goal of all Somatic Therapy.

A 31-day self-care guide is included in the companion guide: "The Blessing: Workbook and Journal of Life with Gratitude." By Naty H.E.A.L.S.

Need self-care but short on time?

Carve out 5 minutes for self-care, no matter how busy you are!

5 MIN SELF-CARE checklist

- [ ] TAKE A FEW DEEP BREATHS
- [ ] BRUSH YOUR HAIR
- [ ] DO SOME STRETCHES
- [ ] DRINK A GLASS OF WATER
- [ ] GRAB A FACE MASK
- [ ] TAKE A QUICK SHOWER
- [ ] WRITE DOWN 7 THINGS YOU ARE GRATEFUL FOR
- [ ] FIND FUNNY VIDEOS WITH CUTE ALPACAS
- [ ] SPEND 5 MIN ORGANISING
- [ ] LIGHT A CANDLE
- [ ] LISTEN TO YOUR FAVOURITE SONG
- [ ] WRITE DOWN YOUR GOALS
- [ ] MAKE YOURSELF A WARM DRINK
- [ ] DANCE LIKE CRAZY
- [ ] TEXT A FRIEND

"Let food be thy medicine and medicine be thy food. "
– Hippocrates   (Hippocrates Quotes. n.d.)

Diet for Successful Somatic Therapy

A huge part of self-care is ensuring you get proper nutrition into your body as consistently as possible. To achieve the best results in healing from stress and trauma, it's essential be conscious of the food you're ingesting. Consider this: if you emptied a cup of oil into your car's gas tank every day, it will start to slow down, ultimately breaking down completely. The same principle applies to your body – consuming unhealthy food can lead to sluggishness and chronic illness. When looking at on your current diet, consider if you should add or remove certain food items from your lifestyle. Your diet is not just food. It includes everything you ingest from any of your senses. This includes the air, personal care products, negative media, and vibes from others.

I was raised in a household that primarily followed a vegetarian diet for some time. However, as I became more independent, my eating habits evolved. I started consuming more processed foods, which affected my body and mind. While I still have a LOVE for french fries, I've become mindful that my food choices impact my physical and mental well-being. Now, I prioritize options that contribute to me feeling better.

Acknowledging that food plays a significant role in your mental and emotional health is vital. The nourishment you consume promptly influences your brain function and can also change your mood and emotions. Maintain top brain function by consuming balanced nutrition with vital items like minerals, micronutrients, and omega-3 fatty acids. You can establish a harmonious relationship by tuning into your body's signals and respecting what it needs. Consuming unhealthy foods will result in you feeling unhealthy. A diet lacking in vital nutrients can negatively affects your emotional stability, leading to mood shifts, and an higher risk of mental health disorders (Toumpanakis et al., 2018).

Consider this: what will you achieve by incorporating positive, mindful practices into your routine while simultaneously consuming unhealthy nutrition? Your Somatic Therapy will produce limited results with an unhealthy diet. By enriching yourself with wholesome foods, you will provide the foundation for the positive and stable emotional state required for Somatic Therapy. Food options can enhance your cognitive functioning, sharpen your focus, and elevate your happiness. Along with exercise, you need this for optimal therapy results.

What about exercise?

Infusing your daily life with movement and exercise can also have a beneficial impact. For example, I use therapeutic swimming and gentle walking to reduce stress and sustain my mobility and flexibility. When you engage in physical activities like walking, dancing, or doing chores around the house, endorphins, which should be called the "euphoria" chemicals, are released by the body, uplifting your mood, easing stress, and can also mitigate the symptoms of depression. Exercise can also help your body move toxins out. Regular movement of any kind can promote better sleep, elevate your self-esteem, and boost your energy levels.

When starting an exercise routine, it is key to make time to get adequate rest at night. The type, intensity, and duration of exercise will vary based on your physical ability, and you should consult your doctor for exercise recommendations. Making exercise a part of your daily routine creates an outlet to release stiffness in the body, focus your mind, and elevate your mood. It's a basic yet impactful method for tending to your holistic well-being. As you can see, Somatic Therapy cannot work alone. You will observe the most significant results when you commit to practicing all of the other ingredients for peace that we've covered so far.

Sleep

Creating healthy sleep patterns is vital for your health and your body's ability to heal. During sleep, the brain creates space for new information, making the sleep cycle crucial. Failure to obtain restful, deep sleep can diminish alertness and awareness, harming your decision-making abilities. You also remove waste from the brain faster during sleep (Xie et al., 2013). In some cases, such as those with bipolar disorder, a lack of sleep can lead to manic episodes.

Learning to navigate your emotions and building positive coping skills is essential to all personal growth. Through mastering emotional self-regulation, you enable yourself to sail through life's problems with composure. Enhanced self-awareness and mindfulness deepen your understanding of thoughts and feelings, allowing for your conscious choices to align with your values. Thrive in the now and let self-care become your focus. With dedication and practice, you can heal and live a life of authenticity and emotional harmony.

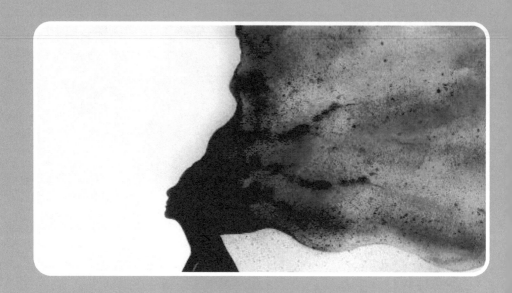

Chapter 4:
Your Body, Brain and Consciousness

What to expect in this chapter:

Autonomic Nervous system (ANS)

Vagus Nerve and The Polyvagal Theory

Hypothalamic-Pituitary-Adrenal Axis

Gray and White Matter

The brain by age and gender

Consciousness

Brainwaves

"Life is really simple, but we insist on making it complicated"
– Confucius   (Confucius Quotes. n.d.)

Harness the power of your brain

When discussing Somatic Therapy, it's not a stretch to study the connectivity of the body, brain, and consciousness. Have you ever stopped and thought about how you do the things you do or why? This chapter goes deeper into the science of it all. Gaining insight into these topics is crucial to fully comprehending what you are currently experiencing, your responses during treatment, and the transformations you'll observe post-therapy. You will gain a more comprehensive grasp of the mind-body connections discussed earlier. We'll cover some basic biology with a focus on the gray-and-white matter of the brain. We'll talk about your nervous system, centering on the vagus nerve.

Additionally, we'll zero into the Polyvagal theory and its relevance to your therapy. You will learn what happens in your Hypothalamic-Pituitary-Adrenal (HPA) axis when stressed. We'll take a fascinating look at the consequences that your gender and age will have on your healing. To fully appreciate your new Somatic Therapy and lifestyle, you must also understand the mysterious concept of consciousness.

This chapter is packed full of terminology; here are some definitions to reference

Neurobiological: Understanding the relationship between the brain's structure, function, and biology. Especially how it influences your behavior, cognition, and other physiological processes in the nervous system. It combines neuroscience and biology to explore the intricate workings of the brain and its impact on the body and mind.

Consciousness: The state of being aware of your thoughts, emotions, sensations, and the external environment. It is the subjective phenomenon of sentience and awareness of your existence and surroundings.

Subconscious: The subconscious is an element of the mind that directs thoughts, feelings, and behaviors without us being aware. It stores memories, instincts, and automatic responses.

Neural connections: Also known as synapses are the lightning-fast communication links between neurons (nerve cells) in the brain and nervous system. These connections are formed by the axons that create synapses, allowing neurons to transmit electrical and chemical signals, enabling information processing, memory formation, and the coordination of bodily functions (Khan Academy, n.d.).

Peripheral Nervous System (PNS): The Peripheral Nervous System is apart from the spinal cord and brain. It joins the central nervous system to the body, allowing for the transmission of sensory information and motor control. It controls your voluntary movements, processes sensory input, and regulates involuntary functions (Khan Academy, n.d.).

The Autonomic Nervous System (ANS): A division of the Peripheral Nervous System that guides and controls involuntary bodily tasks, such as gastric, heart rate, respiratory, and glandular activities. It operates automatically and regulates your bodily processes to maintain your internal balance, also known as homeostasis.

Homeostasis: The body's ability to maintain stable internal variables, like pH, temperature, and fluid balance, despite external changes. It involves self-regulating mechanisms that ensure optimal somatic function, enabling you to adapt to varying environments (Gibbons, 2019).

The Ventral Vagus Nerve: Part of the Autonomic Nervous System involved in your "social engagement" response. It has nerve connections from the diaphragm to the brainstem via upward pathways. It steers your social interactions, emotional regulation, and expressions, promoting a sense of connection and relaxation.

"We don't laugh because we're happy - we're happy because we laugh."

~ William James   (William James Quotes. n.d.)

Tune into your automatic machine

Your autopilot, known as the Autonomic Nervous System (ANS), is a component of the Peripheral Nervous System that primarily functions involuntarily, overseeing your internal organs and glands (Gibbons, 2019).

The nervous system's natural, intricate wiring is much like the delicate circuits inside your phone, transmitting signals seamlessly, powering life's functions like that phone.

The Peripheral Nervous System (PNS) manages the sensory and motor signals between the body and the central nervous system, consisting of the spinal cord and brain. It manages and integrates data from the PNS, governing your bodily functions while aiding your cognitive and motor functions. This is where all the action happens (Khan Academy, n.d.).

The PNS is like the delicate network of wires in your phone, branching out to every corner, transmitting messages from the central hub, ensuring seamless communication and response.

The ANS is an intriguing and essential part of your body's operating system; it works behind the scenes to seamlessly keep you moving. It is a elaborate network of nerves and bundles of ganglia that control your automatic bodily functions. Nerve cells bundle together to form ganglia. They are responsible for relaying and processing sensory and autonomic or "involuntary" information. It controls the functions that work automatically like heartbeat, respiratory, and gastric activities.

The Ganglia, much like the nodes in your phone's wiring, are nature's hubs of communication, processing signals efficiently, connecting the threads of life and technology with seamless precision." The ANS maintains a delicate balance to keep your body functioning optimally. This system is what keeps you alive, so you need it in good shape for your survival.

The autonomic nervous system exists in three distinct primary states: the Sympathetic, Parasympathetic, and Enteric systems.

Sympathetic Nervous System (SNS): This gears you up in moments of stress or peril, prompting the fight-flight-freeze response. It readies your body for action by recognizing stress or potential dangers. The body evolved the Sympathetic Nervous System (SNS) as a primal response mechanism in our ancestors to ensure survival in the many dangerous scenarios they faced. Imagine running and hiding from an ancient predator without a properly working nervous system!

Activation of the Sympathetic Nervous System (SNS) points to an increased heart rate, dilated pupils, and slowed digestion. It also releases stress hormones like cortisol, adrenaline, and noradrenaline (Feenstra, 2000). Adrenaline serves as a natural pain killer, allowing you to exceed your typical pain thresholds to face the threat. Meanwhile, cortisol aids in reducing inflammation, contributing to your pain relief. In the freeze response, this system is active during the initial phase of the perceived threat.

Parasympathetic Nervous System (PNS): It is responsible for the "rest and digest" response, aka state of relaxation, recovery, and digestion. It is pivotal in returning to baseline functioning by orchestrating various physiological responses that promote a calm state (Müller et al., 2017). Notable actions include slowing your heart rate following stress, aiding digestion through increased saliva and stomach activity, and causing pupil constriction when the body isn't in a fight-flight-freeze mode. This is why resting is so essential. Additionally, it eases bladder and bowel functions, supports sexual arousal, and can diminish stress hormones such as cortisol (Gibbons, 2019). The PNS conserves energy, boosts your immune system, and restores depleted energy reserves after exertion. It's a fundamental component in the body's ability to recuperate and regain equilibrium post-stress. In the freeze response, this system sustains your immobility and preserves your energy. It is thought that immobility or freeze aims to help you avoid detection from predators or threats.

Enteric Nervous System (ENS): It is often considered the "third" branch of the ANS, although it functions independently. This "second brain" is a complex network of nerves and neurons in your gut that govern the gastrointestinal tract's functioning. It receives input from the SNS and PNS and reacts to your emotional vibe, controlling digestion and other gastrointestinal processes (Gibbons, 2019). Have you ever gotten upset and lost your appetite? This explains it. While the ENS doesn't directly participate in the fight-flight-freeze response, it can indirectly affect it. Intense stress or fear can influence digestive processes, potentially leading to symptoms like shifts in bowel regularity or discomfort in your digestive system. (Gershon, 1999).

Together, the states of the ANS collaborate to adjust and maintain your various involuntary bodily functions. A seamless balance and coordination between the systems is crucial for your body's overall health and wellness. You can aid the ANS through deep breathing, meditation, and self-care.

Ever wonder what happens in your brain to produce the fight-flight-freeze response?

Here is a brief description.

Situated in the temporal lobes of your brain, the amygdala plays a pivotal role in handling emotions, particularly those linked to your survival instincts and fear. When it perceives a threat, the amygdala communicates through neural pathways to the hypothalamus, sending both chemical signals and electrical impulses (Heck & Handa, 2018). The hypothalamus is pivotal in regulating hormone release from the pituitary gland (Gimpl & Fahrenholz, 2001). By triggering the Autonomic Nervous System, these signals set off the fight-flight response through the activation of the Sympathetic Nervous System

(Gibbons, 2019). The pons and the locus coeruleus are two brain parts vital to the stress response. The pons is a structure in your brainstem made of nuclei and nerve fibers. The pons are crucial in coordinating your movement, transmitting sensory information, and regulating your essential bodily functions such as breathing, hearing, and eye control. The locus coeruleus is a part of the brainstem engaged in producing and releasing the neurotransmitter and hormone noradrenaline. During the stress response, the locus coeruleus located in the pons sends noradrenaline, also known as norepinephrine, to the brain (Aston-Jones et al., 2000).

Norepinephrine is crucial in improving your cognitive functions and equipping the body to handle stress-induced demands. It increases your brain's processing speed, which aids in quicker decision-making and responses. Additionally, the heightened activity of the frontal lobe, influenced by norepinephrine, improves your problem-solving, reasoning, and other high-level cognitive functions (Brassard et al., 2014). It also boosts your senses, helping you to be more sensitive and insightful to things you touch, see, smell, hear, and taste. Simultaneously, releasing cortisol, another stress hormone, further contributes to your body's adaptive response. Cortisol temporarily suppresses non-essential functions, enhances your memory, and maintains homeostasis. Cortisol and adrenaline which is also known as epinephrine, are primarily released by the adrenal glands during the body's stress response (McCarty, 2016). Situated on the upper portion of each kidney, the adrenal glands secrete these into the bloodstream when the body perceives a threat or experiences a high-stress situation (Gimpl & Fahrenholz, 2001). This triggers physiological changes such as heightening energy, the rerouting of blood circulation to key muscles, and a raised heart rate. When the threat is too overwhelming for your brain to manage, it begins to change and slow down. During the freeze response, the frontal lobe areas become much less active, resulting in a sense of immobilization. This is because the frontal lobe governs your voluntary movements, making you feel "stuck." Your ability to vocalize, understand language, and make sound judgments may also be affected. Meanwhile, the amygdala ramps up its activity resulting in intensified alertness and powerful emotions. It's crucial to acknowledge that the freeze response's precise mechanisms and contributing factors are still under ongoing research.

Now it's time to explore everyone's favorite nerve (or at least it should be). The Vagus Nerve.

image by: (JohnPaulCook, 2019)

"We are shaped by our thoughts; we become what we think. When the mind is pure, joy follows like a shadow that never leaves" - Buddha (Buddha Quotes. n.d.)

The Vagus Nerve

This nerve is tied to the most profound parts of what makes you...you. The vagus nerve is like the body's natural "reset button," a fascinating neural pathway that not only influences essential bodily functions but also has a calming effect, like a cool breeze on a hot day, restoring your balance and tranquility as it cools you down. The vagus nerve is a notable component of the Autonomic Nervous System. Sometimes also called the Vagal Pathway or Cranial Nerve X. Going forward. I'll refer to this only as the vagus nerve for ease of understanding. The name is derived from the Latin word for "wandering" because of its broad distribution across the body. It is one of the longest and most important nerves that you have. An intricate and interconnected network influences many aspects of your natural behavior. The nerve originates in the brainstem and extends to assorted vital organs, like the digestive system, lungs and heart. The vagus nerve helps to manage many involuntary functions. It significantly affects your body's stress response and emotional regulation (Porges, 2003). A pivotal role is played by the the vagus nerve in the Parasympathetic Nervous System, which promotes rest, relaxation, and recovery. Its proper functioning is essential for maintaining balance within your body or homeostasis (W. Neuhuber & Berthoud, 2022). That is why a healthy vagus nerve is so vital to your Somatic Therapy and trauma-healing success.

Vagal Tone

Vagal tone is all about the intensity level of the nerve. Think of your vagal tone as the volume level of the vagus nerve. It's a gauge of how well your body's relaxation and calming system is working. A higher tone nerve indicates proper body functioning and a better ability to recover from stress (Beauchaine, 2001). A less active, lower-tone nerve means that you may have a reduced ability to manage stress and an increased chance of health issues such as depression, chronic stress, anxiety, inflammatory conditions, digestive disorders, fatigue, lowered pain tolerance, autoimmune diseases, mood and sleep disorders and heart health issues (Weber et al., 2010).

Here are some easy ways to increase your vagal tone:

Deep Breathing:

Practice "diaphragmatic" deep breathing. The diaphragm is a large core muscle positioned beneath the rib cage that aids you when pushing air out of the lungs. Activate your vagus nerve by practicing slow, deep diaphragmatic breathing instead of shallow chest breaths (Zaccaro et al., 2018). This will help regulate your nervous system and encourages a tranquil and grounded state; you will learn about breathwork in Chapter 5.

Positive Social Interactions:

Engaging in meaningful conversations, sharing laughter, expressing kindness, and creating positive social experiences can all activate the Ventral Vagus Nerve. Even smiling can help.

Cold Exposure:

Exposure to cold, such as chilly showers or submersion in cold water, can stimulate the vagus nerve. Even an ice pack on your neck, just below your earlobe, and behind your jawline on either side of your throat can help. Keep in mind when using the ice pack, start with brief exposures of 30 seconds to 1 minute, gradually increasing to up to 15 minutes. You can also try drinking ice water (Chavan, 2017).

If you want to try cold exposure, the training process could take a while as your mind and body learn to embrace the sensation. It's important to dedicate time to just being still and mindful, allowing yourself to experience the calming effects. To train for cold exposure, slowly expose yourself to decreased temperatures and increase your daily tolerance. Start with limited sessions, like brief cold showers or time in a cool environment. Practice controlled breathing and progress slowly. Safety is crucial, so listen to your body and stop if uncomfortable. Cold exposure is not for everyone, particularly people with medical concerns. Please consult with a healthcare professional before trying. I've seen some athletes stay in an ice bath for up to an hour with professional supervision. Some have even reported falling into deep meditative states during extended ice baths.

Chanting, Singing and Humming:

Activities like singing, humming, chanting, and even gargling can activate muscles and stimulate your vagus nerve. Specifically, forms of chanting or singing that entail extended exhalation may have this effect. Any singing that involves deep and rhythmic breathing should help. Chanting "Om" (Aum) is a great starter. The "Om" mantra is fundamental to many Eastern spiritual practices. Repeating "Om" with a prolonged "ooooooommmmm" sound can promote relaxation and vagal activation. Chanting "Ah" and "Ooh" vowel sounds slowly and deliberately could also work. You can experiment with different vowel sounds to see which resonates best with you. My trauma therapist taught me a great way to cope with a panic attack. She said to hug myself tight and hum my favorite song. It was a simple and effective tool. The soothing effect helped stimulate the vagus nerve, helping me feel calm and safe.

Avoid Chronic Stress:

Chronic stress can lower vagal tone. Implement stress management skills like mindfulness, time management, and setting boundaries to reduce chronic stressors in your life. Constant pressure stresses your Nervous System and wears it down, misfiring the signals and creating illness and disease (Beauchaine, 2001). Refer to the mindfulness exercises in Chapter 2. Vagus Nerve Stimulation can even improve your memory (Sun et al., 2017). Please note that these practices do not treat severe vagus nerve dysregulation. They could help activate the vagus nerve based on the root cause and intensity of your issue. Nerve regeneration may occur over time. However, there may be a need for surgical procedures to address the issue.

Relaxing with a loved one or friend? Consider co-regulation exercises. You can engage in co-regulation exercises to practice regulating your Autonomic Nervous System together. You can do it with a professional, friend, partner, or loved one. Make sure it's someone who will encourage and care for you. Co-regulation means you are doing these exercises with support and the feeling of safety of another (Williamson, 2023). Connecting with others and knowing they "have your back" is key for your joy and well-being. For me, life is all about relationships! (Relationships with healthy boundaries, of course.)

Co-regulation exercises include attentive listening, recognizing another's feelings, practicing deep breathing, and nonverbal gestures such as maintaining focused eye contact and gentle touch (Williamson, 2023). Co-regulation practices are powerful tools that can deepen the connection in your relationship. It's important to note that improving vagal tone is a gradual process, and individual responses may vary. Consistently using these practices can help enhance your vagal tone. Talk with a healthcare practioner if you have questions about your vagus nerve or medical conditions.

image by: (Recurrent Laryngeal nerve.svg, 2014)

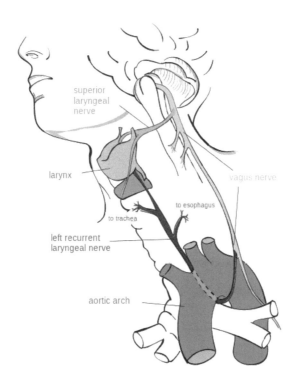

The vagus nerve can be broken down into three states or hierarchical circuits: the Dorsal Vagus Nerve, Ventral Vagal Nerve, and the Sympathetic Nervous system. A hierarchical circuit refers to a structured system of linked neural pathways that operate in a specific order. Think of a hierarchical circuit like different grades of sandpaper lined up in a particular order. Each grade serves a purpose in smoothing a surface, just as each neural pathway plays a role in processing information in a structured sequence. The top of the circuit includes our most evolved and most socially engaged states of being, while the bottom of the circuit represents our most primitive and survival states of being.

The Ventral Vagus Circuit has neural pathways and connections within the Ventral Vagal Complex responsible for regulating your socialization and emotional responses. The Ventral Vagal Complex is a collection of brain structures and pathways associated with this circuit. Nicknamed the "Social Engagement System," we need this for connecting with others and managing stress effectively (Denver, 2004). The Ventral Vagus Circuit is a myelinated nerve that regulates the muscles in your head and face, including your facial gestures and other non-verbal cues. It enables the Ventral Vagal Complex, which cues your mind and helps propel your social interactions, nonverbal communication, and emotional connection. This is what permits you to associate with fellow beings in a calm and socially appropriate manner. It's what enables you to effectivly communicate. Once this nerve is activated, this circuit promotes feelings of safety, bonding, and relaxation (W. Neuhuber & Berthoud, 2022). This gives you a sense of security and confidence in social environments.

Curious to know what it feels like when this circuit is activated? Pause and reflect on a moment of genuine laughter, when your body was entirely relaxed, how you felt when someone you love walked into the room, or when a hug felt oh-so-good. How would you describe those sensations?

To me, it's one of the most rewarding aspects of the human experience.

The Sympathetic Nervous System circuit is a nerve network that responds to stress by initializing your fight-or-flight response. Think of moments like being chased by a strange dog, hearing a startling noise, or, for some, it activates during public speaking. This circuit initiates a stress response that helps you either confront or escape the threat. If you have ever felt rage, panic, or anxiety, this system has kicked in.

When was the last time this has happened to you?

Parts of this response are autonomic, which refers to the involuntary or automatic functions and processes, including unconscious mechanisms in the brainstem and hypothalamic. This part of the forebrain is involved in processing emotions and memory. The second aspect of the response involves conscious attention mechanisms in the higher brain functions, including your abilities for sustained, divided, and selective attention. This system raises your heart rate, heightens alertness, induces sweating, dilates your pupils, mobilizes your muscles, and halts your digestion. It recognizes your body's energy needs and shifts into a protective mode.

The Dorsal Vagus Nerve circuit is a component of the ANS that is associated with the "immobilization" response, aka the "freeze" or "shutdown" response. It is a network of nerves and pathways related to the dorsal or back branch of the vagus nerve (Porges, 2009).

It kicks in when you face moments of extreme danger or are completely overwhelmed with stress. For example, it activates during times of physical abuse, trauma, or life-threatening situations (Bracha, 2004). This would include times that you have felt trapped or completely helpless or if you have ever felt emotionally "frozen," dissociated, or numb. This "rest and digest" part of the nerve may be involved in why those with trauma also often have upset stomachs and digestive concerns. Activating the Dorsal Vagus nerve's shutdown response is a primitive survival mechanism (Cannon, 1915). It's just another way that the brain tries to protect you.

The Dorsal Vagus Complex is a distinct bundle of nerve cells in the brainstem that is an element of the Dorsal Vagus Nerve circuit.

The Dorsal Vagus Complex is like a hidden superhero in the nervous system, quietly ensuring the body's calm and cool state. The complex is a critical component within the larger circuit that contributes to maintaining your body's homeostasis (Porges, 2009). Research is being conducted to determine if excessive or chronic activation of this response can leads to conditions like Post-Traumatic Stress Disorder (PTSD), Fibromyalgia, and dissociative disorders (Rothschild, 2000).

Understanding these different states of being is vital as they relate to your unique response to stress and social interaction. Consider instances like sweaty palms on a first date or in nerve-wracking meetings, feeling bashful around others, becoming momentarily frozen when someone you're fond of addresses you, or experiencing a temporary loss of hearing during moments of intense stress. Has this ever happened to you?

SAFE:

Feeling Safe, open to social engagement and play (Parasympathetic Ventral Vagal System)

MOBILIZED:

Mobilized in response to a perceived threat, ready to fight or flee (Sympathetic Nervous system)

IMMOBILIZED:

Immobilized in response to an extreme threat, shut-down and unable to move (Parasympathetic Dorsal Vagal System)

image by:(-luffyboy-, 2021)

Mind your Vagus nerve!

A compromised vagus nerve can lead to Autonomic Nervous System imbalances, manifesting a full range of physical and mental challenges such as:

Heart Problems:

Your heart rate and rhythm is managed in part by the vagus nerve. It's disruption can lead to arrhythmias, palpitations, and abnormal heart rate responses to physical and emotional stress. Ever notice the beat of the heart when you are afraid? How about after a relaxing bath or walk in nature?

Digestive Issues:

The vagus nerve performs a key part in regulating the digestive process, stimulating stomach acid production and promoting gastrointestinal movement and contraction. Dysregulation can lead to problems such as gastroparesis which is delayed stomach emptying or varied gastric disturbances. This is why people who have high stress usually have stomach issues.

Breathing Difficulties:

The vagus nerve is connected to respiratory function, and its disruption may lead to breathing difficulties, especially during increased stress. (W. Neuhuber & Berthoud, 2022). Think of your breathing when you are afraid or having a panic attack as opposed to when you are most relaxed.

Blood Pressure Instability:

Vagus nerve disruption could trigger fluctuations in blood pressure, contributing to low blood pressure when standing also know as orthostatic hypotension. When you're stressed, the heart has to boost its labors to circulate your blood to the right places, weakening your heart muscles over time and creating illness and disease.

Speech and Swallowing Difficulties:

Dysregulation of the Vagus Nerve can result in speech, hoarseness, and swallowing difficulties. This is because the Vagus Nerve plays a role in swallowing by coordinating the complex muscle movements involved in the process. It senses the stretching of the esophagus and communicates with the brain to trigger the swallowing reflex. The Vagus Nerve also controls the throat and esophagus muscles, ensuring the synchronized contraction and relaxation needed for safe and efficient swallowing.

Gastroesophageal Reflux Disease (GERD):

The vagus nerve helps control the lower esophageal sphincter, and its disruption can contribute to GERD, causing acid reflux, heartburn, and more. A muscular ring known as the lower esophageal sphincter (LES) behaves as a shield between the stomach and esophagus. In many cases of GERD, the vagus nerve might not function optimally, leading to a weakened LES. In instances where the lower esophageal sphincter doesn't seal tightly, stomach acid can travel to the esophagus, resulting in heartburn and discomfort.

Mood and Mental Health:

Mood and emotional responses are under the regulatory influence of the vagus nerve. Its disruption may be associated with various mood disorders and an heightened vulnerability to mental health concerns (Beauchaine, 2001). Stimulation of the Vagus Nerve can alleviate symptoms of depression and anxiety. Additionally, the vagus nerve participates in the creation and control of neurotransmitters such as GABA and serotonin, significant for emotional stabilization (W. Neuhuber & Berthoud, 2022).

Inflammation and Immune Response:

The vagus nerve's activation can help regulate your inflammatory response and immune function. Disruption of the vagus nerve may affect your body's ability to manage inflammation. When faced with physical damage, viruses, bacteria and disease, the body activates inflammation as a natural safeguard. It involves processes that protect, remove damaged cells, and promote healing. When the inflammatory response is activated, chemical signals prompt an increased blood flow, causing redness, warmth, swelling, and pain in the area. Though brief amounts of inflammation can have benefits, chronic inflammation due to stress or an unhealthy diet can be highly detrimental. It's linked to health issues like heart disease, autoimmune disorders, and certain cancers (W. Neuhuber & Berthoud, 2022). Effectively managing any chronic inflammation is essential for healing. You need this nerve for your Somatic Therapy in so many ways, including your emotional expression and regulation, mind-body awareness, trauma healing, and breathwork, to name a few.

Be Careful! Your vagus nerve may be compromised by the following

Surgery:

Surgery to the check or neck, including thyroid surgery, cardiac surgery, or surgeries to remove tumors, can sometimes lead to accidental injury to the vagus nerve.

Physical Trauma:

Trauma affecting the head, neck, or chest region, such as those sustained in car accidents, domestic violence, or falls, can yield vagus nerve damage.

Infections:

Certain infections, like Lyme disease viral or bacterial infections, may cause inflammation and disrupt the vagus nerve.

Chronic Illnesses:

Nerve damage, including dysregulation of the vagus nerve, is a potential outcome of disorders like Multiple Sclerosis, autoimmune disorders or diabetes

Neck or Throat Radiation:

Targeting cancer in the neck or throat area through radiation therapy can inadvertently damage the vagus nerve.

Gastrointestinal Surgeries:

Surgeries involving the stomach or intestines, such as gastric bypass surgery, may sometimes cause injury to the vagus nerve.

Tumors or Growths:

Benign or cancerous growths in the neck, chest, or abdomen may compress or disrupt the vagus nerve. This disruption can lead to lower heart rate, digestive issues such as nausea and vomiting, low blood pressure, low heart rate, and problems swallowing or speaking

Degenerative Disorders:

Certain neurodegenerative disorders may affect the vagus nerve over time, such as Parkinson's disease.

I'm sure you can see how understanding and supporting the vitality and performance of your Vagus Nerve is significant for promoting optimal Somatic Therapy conditions. The Vagus Nerve, the key component of your social engagement system, is further described in the Polyvagal Theory that we will explore next. You will feel more settled, grounded, curious, and compassionate when this nerve is activated.

"No one saves us but ourselves. No one can and no one may. We ourselves must walk the path" - Buddha (Buddha Quotes. n.d.)

The Polyvagal Theory

You might be curious how so much knowledge was aquired about the interconnection between your ANS, Vagus Nerve, and stress. It took a long time from the concept of "fight or flight," as explained by W. B. Cannon in 1915, to the unfolding of the Polyvagal Theory by Dr. Stephen Porges in the early 1990s (McCarty, 2016, Chapter 4). The theory explains the complex connection between the ANS, your social behaviors and the vagus nerve. It has revolutionized the treatment of trauma and healing by shedding light on these key relationships (Porges, 2003).

It deeply focuses on the three states, aka branches of the ANS, each representing a different level of evolutionary response to stress that we covered in the vagus nerve section (W. Neuhuber & Berthoud, 2022). It provides an intriguing perspective on how shifts in your ANS can influence the scope of your behaviors in response to external stressors. The Ventral Vagal Nerve (safe and social engagement response), the Sympathetic Nervous System (mobilized / "flight or fight" response), and the Dorsal Vagus Nerve (immobilized / freeze response).

It also provides a better understanding of coping mechanisms, such as dissociation. Dissociation means feeling detached from yourself in someway (Foa & Hearst-Ikeda, 1996). One of its key achievements is its ability to help you effectively identify your triggers to better manage your stress. By recognizing whether you're in a state of safety, threat, or immobilization, this theory has paved the way for your success. It provides the essential insight for effective healing and growth.

It's crucial to acknowledge that various traditional medicine systems, like Ayurveda and Traditional Chinese Medicine, have always recognized the significance and interplay of the Autonomic Nervous System in healing, even if they didn't employ the term "ANS."

Further insights into these different approaches will be explored in Chapter 8.

"Anybody can become angry - that is easy, but to be angry with the right person and to the right degree and at the right time and for the right purpose, and in the right way - that is not within everybody's power and is not easy."

– Aristotle   (Aristotle Quotes. n.d.)

Superpower of the HPA

Like the Sympathetic Nervous System, the Hypothalamic-Pituitary-Adrenal Axis (HPA) is important in regulating your stress reaction. It's the body's internal command center, like a sophisticated control panel in a high-tech spaceship. It controls and helps coordinate the body's response to stress, releasing hormones that regulate various functions. Compared to the Sympathetic Nervous System, it responds slower, taking minutes to hours. It primarily releases cortisol, vital for long-term stress regulation and recovery (Heck & Handa, 2018).

In contrast, the Sympathetic Nervous System operates through nerve impulses, reacting rapidly for immediate physiological changes. The HPA Axis helps you adjust to long-term stress. At the same time, the Sympathetic Nervous System focuses on your immediate survival needs. The HPA Axis activates your body's systems when encountering threats, new experiences, or meaningful moments. The HPA Axis involves hormonal signaling between the Hypothalamus, Pituitary Gland, and Adrenal Cortex glands to form a "management team" for your stress. The team's job is to detect stress, send messages, and release hormones to help you act when in need (Stress System Malfunction Could Lead to Serious, Life Threatening Disease, 2002).

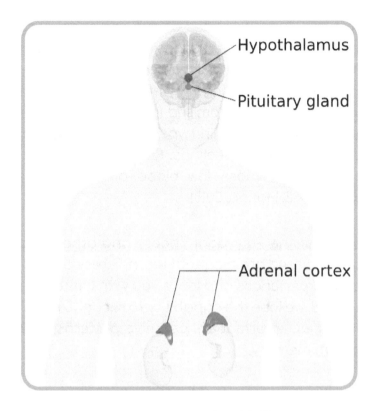

(Anatomography, 2015)

The HPA axis regulates the secretion of hormones like cortisol to support your bodies stress-handling abilities and maintain somatic balance. Cortisol is a natural product of the adrenal cortex glands, released in response to stress. It heightens alertness, provides a rapid energy surge, and damps down inflammation when you need it most. Cortisol reduces inflammation and protects us from swelling during an injury. However, this management team can sometimes work unauthorized overtime, causing major health issues (Stress System Malfunction Could Lead to Serious, Life Threatening Disease, 2002).

An HPA Axis imbalance (elevated or reduced cortisol) can occur due to trauma, PTSD, chronic stress, illness, poor diet, or sleep issues. Extending periods of stress can generate an excess of cortisol, which can have negative effects (Yehuda et al., 1991). These may include a compromised immune system, heightened appetite leading to weight gain, hypertension, along with anxious thoughts and depressive feelings. Reduced cortisol levels can cause fatigue, weight loss, low blood pressure, anxiety, and depression.(Heck & Handa, 2018).

From looking at the Polyvagal Theory and other theories, we know that a stressed brain cannot learn. Stress can lead you to overreact to experiences and leave you with limited responses. When stressed, we lose the capability to recognize subtle cues, store and access information, perceive patterns, and access our long-term memory.

Understanding the underlying biology allows you to appreciate the effectiveness of mindfulness and self-care practices. A well-functioning HPA axis is crucial to the Somatic Therapy healing process. The techniques you've acquired will aid in stress reduction, ensuring your HPA system functions optimally and supporting the progress of your Somatic Therapy. Now, let's delve into understanding different regions of the brain.

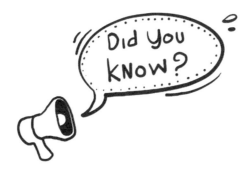

Shrinkage of the Brain: Prolonged exposure to stress hormones can lead to the diminishing of the hippocampus, the area of the brain responsible for information storage and learning. This has the potential to compromise your cognitive function and elevate your susceptibility to mental health issues (Park & Reuter-Lorenz, 2009).

Gray matter, White matter, and Myelinated Axons

The brain is a self-organizing system continually shaped over time by your ongoing experiences. As you know, the Central Nervous System includes your spinal cord and brain. Gray and white matter are extraordinary brain components responsible for processing all available sensory input (Khan Academy, n.d.). This provides you with a complete comprehension of the world around you.

Gray matter refers to brain tissue containing the neurons, blood vessels, and immune cells responsible for sensory processing, motor control, decision-making, memory, and more. It allows you to think, see, hear, and move.

White matter is comprised of bundles of nerve fibers, known as axons, enveloped in a white, insulating, protective substance called myelin. This intricate structure is formed by over 80,000 miles of individual myelinated nerve fibers or axons. This network helps the gray matter regions communicate by transmitting electrical signals (Khan Academy, n.d.). The gray and white matter could be compared to an office building. Imagine the framework of the building as your body's framework.

The gray and white matter are parts of the electrical system within the building. The gray matter compares to the electrical control room of the building. In contrast, the white matter is the heavy-duty electrical wiring that speeds up the communication between different brain cells. White matter also helps nourish and give structure like drywall to the connections of the gray matter cells. Finally, the individual myelinated nerve fibers or Axons act as the output cords that send signals out to the body. They can be compared to the internet running through the building, connecting everything to the outside world, like sending an email or having a meeting online. Just as vital as these parts are for a building, they are equally essential to running your body. Now that you better understand the structures that control your life. What happens to these structures over time?

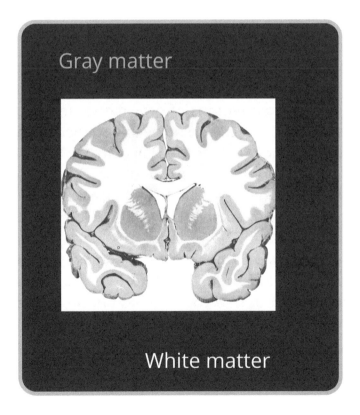

Image:(JonesChristiana, 2022)

Changes in brain connectivity as we age

As we get older, the gray and white matter changes. When you were born, your brain was unassembled in a way. As each day went by and your brain matured, it created space for your growth. As a child, when your brain was maturing, higher states of consciousness were brought into your life (De Bellis et al., 2001). The integrated functioning of 100 billion neurons supports the reality of your states of consciousness throughout your lifespan. (BioBeats, 2021)

To optimize the effectiveness of Somatic Therapy, it's crucial to prioritize brain health as you age. White matter volume typically diminishes with age, potentially impacting information processing and cognitive abilities (Park & Reuter-Lorenz, 2009). Certain regions of gray matter may experience shrinkage, while others may display indications of thickening or increased volume over time (De Bellis et al., 2001). Your lifestyle choices, genetic predisposition, and the general health of your brain can impact the extent and pace of these changes. Engaging in a healthy lifestyle can potentially slow down age-related brain changes. This includes regular physical exercise, good sleep & diet, stress management, and mental stimulation (Exclamation & Exclamation, 2021). Now that you have a deeper understanding about how your age can make a difference in your therapy, it's time to explore the role of gender.

Will your brain's gender make a difference in your Somatic Therapy?

It's intriguing to see that studies have found differences in gray and white matter between males and females.

Female Identity

In females, there might be a slightly greater volume of gray matter in areas associated to social dynamics and linguistic communication, possibly due to larger language centers in the hippocampus. Additionally, they may exhibit enhanced connectivity within brain networks associated with social and emotional processing (Bell et al., 2006). This explains why females often demonstrate heightened emotional awareness and can swiftly discern subtle emotional cues compared to males. Elevated estrogen levels in females lead to increased release of oxytocin, reducing the flight-or-fight response (Ordaz & Luna, 2012). Oxytocin, present in higher levels in females, is the hormone and neurotransmitter referred to as the "love" or "bonding" hormone. Those with higher oxytocin were shown to be more generous as well. (Zak et al., 2007).

You can release oxytocin by getting a foot massage or enjoying a nurturing touch, such as hugging or hand-holding. Even hugging your pets can increase levels of this feel-good hormone and lower the stress hormone cortisol. Oxytocin has a vital duty when it comes to social bonding, trust, and maternal behavior, as it's the same hormone released in massive levels to bond mothers and babies during childbirth (Gimpl & Fahrenholz, 2001.)

High levels of oxytocin transform the stress response in the HPA axis to a caregiving response nicknamed the "tend-and-befriend." "Tend" involves caregiving, while "befriend" seeks social connections. This response emphasizes communal bonds and balance during stress (Baron-Cohen, 2004). For instance, the "tend and befriend" response involves someone stepping into a caregiver or helper role or seeking emotional support and connection from others in times of stress. This response offers an alternative to the "fight or flight" instinct by providing an emotional coping mechanism rather than a physical one.

Male identity

In males, a slightly greater volume of gray matter may be in brain areas associated with spatial processing and mathematical reasoning (Bell et al., 2006). Additionally, male brains might have a higher quantity of white matter and generate elevated cortisol and adrenaline levels compared to females (Davis et al., 2003). This heightened adrenaline act as both a neurotransmitter and hormone, released in reaction to stress or danger for a quick physical reaction (Baron-Cohen, 2004). Additionally, some studies suggest that males may have higher white matter connectivity within brain networks related to spatial skills (Ordaz & Luna, 2012). Males are well suited for doing rather than dealing with emotions. Elevated adrenaline levels result in a surge in heart rate, tense muscles, and a redirection of blood flow from digestion to muscles in stressful situations. Raised testosterone levels in males trigger the release of oxytocin, influencing traits like assertiveness, aggression, and emotional regulation (Gimpl & Fahrenholz,

2001). Intriguingly, heightened oxytocin in men might be linked to hypersexual disorder. (Monaco, 2022).

But what about transgendered people and others in the LGBTQIA + community?

Interestingly, research shows that a person's gray matter and brain anatomy can influence their gender identity. Gender identity is the personal, internal sense of being either male or female (Luders et al., 2009). Brain anatomy may deviate from what is typically associated with one's biological sex, aligning more closely with the anatomy of the gender they identify with (Kurth et al., 2022). It's crucial to emphasize that your gender and gender identity don't dictate your cognitive abilities or behaviors. Regardless of these factors, healing is possible. However, understanding how your biology may intersect with your treatment is valuable information.

Your Consciousness and Somatic Therapy

Consciousness is a pivotal aspect of Somatic Therapy. While the term is widely recognized, few are aware that it's a quality that can be expanded and developed. As you know, consciousness is a elaborate and multifaceted phenomenon that entails being perceptive of your emotions, thoughts, environment, and senses. It is your personal experience of awareness and allows you to interact with the world around you. Consciousness relies on your whole nervous system to function correctly (Block & Dennett, 1993). The goal is to not just have any consciousness but to have a clear and healthy consciousness. It can be made clearer and expanded by the practice of Somatic Therapy and certain other activities.

The nervous system has a immediate effect on the clarity and healthiness of your consciousness. Clarity implies having a precise understanding and heightened awareness of your surroundings, emotions, and thoughts. Numerous factors, including your age, lifestyle choices, and physical conditions, can influence the clarity of your consciousness. While certain factors may be unavoidable, it's crucial to minimize those within your control. For instance, excessive alcohol and drug consumption, inadequate nutrition and sleep, lack of exercise, and neglecting your mindfulness routine can impact your consciousness. Remember, every action in life yields a reaction. This is key in Somatic Therapy, as consciousness enables you to be aware of bodily experiences and sensations right as they occur in the present moment. Heightened consciousness empowers you to recognize how emotions and past experiences are being manifested in your body.

Another key concept is the subconscious mind, which is a component of consciousness but operates beneath conscious awareness. It's where all your thoughts, feelings, memories, and automatic processes that influence your behavior and experiences are held. You may not notice the workings of the subconscious mind; however, they significantly impact your thoughts, emotions, behaviors, and life (Block & Dennett, 1993).

Automatic responses generated from the subconscious mind occur regardless of conscious thought or deliberate intent (Lanius et al., 2017). These responses occur almost instantaneously and are instinctual or ingrained in you through your past experiences (A New Theory of Consciousness: The Mind Exists as a Field Connected to the Brain - SAND, n.d.). For example, swiftly withdrawing your hand from a hot surface or flinching when you are startled are the automatic responses of the subconscious mind. It holds significant sway in trauma recovery by housing your traumatic memories, emotions, and bodily sensations.

Delving into your subconscious proves crucial in trauma healing for various reasons including:

1. Integrating Traumatic Experiences: **Traumatic memories and emotions often linger fragmented and unprocessed in the subconscious. Consciously acknowledging them facilitates integration and resolution.**

2. Unearthing Repressed Emotions: **The subconscious may conceal intense, suppressed emotions linked to the trauma.**

3. Reprogramming Maladaptive Beliefs: **Trauma can instill negative core beliefs, typically anchored in your subconscious. Illuminating them allows you to reframe and reprogram these beliefs.**

4. Regulating the Nervous System: **The subconscious**

governs your autonomic responses and nervous system patterns tied to trauma.

5. Empowerment and Regaining Agency: Understanding the subconscious facets of trauma will reveal that your reactions and behaviors are learned responses that can be changed.

Here are some interesting facts about the subconscious mind:

My Perpetual Vigilance: The subconscious mind operates endlessly, never taking a break or resting. It oversees your vital bodily functions like heart rate, circulation, and digestion day and night.

Dominant Influence: Remarkably, the subconscious exerts a staggering 95% control over our lives. This means that the majority of our actions and decisions occur without our conscious awareness.

Habitual Realm: Habit formation is a natural process, largely orchestrated by the subconscious. It quietly carries out these routines, often without your conscious realization.

Present-Centric: The subconscious mind is firmly rooted in the present moment. It redirects focus from future or past worries; this helps you have a grounded awareness.

Attentive Listener: Ever-attentive, the subconscious mind listens intently without respite. (Lanius et al., 2017). It takes your self-talk at face value, whether it's self-encouragement or self-criticism. Thus, when you believe in your capabilities or doubt them, you're likely correct.

You can expand your consciousness with the following practices:

Explore Your Beliefs:

Question your beliefs and assumptions. Listen to and be open to new perspectives and ideas, allowing yourself to grow and evolve.

Emotional Intelligence:

Dedicate time to exploring and managing your emotional responses. Figure out how they influence your thoughts and behaviors before reacting. Work on active listening and clear communication. Act mindfully and consciously.

Seek Feedback:

Get opinions from trusted friends, family, or advisors to gain insights into how others perceive you.

Stay Curious:

Set the intention to stay curious and open-minded, and always seek to deepen your self-awareness and broaden your perspective on the world..

Remember that expanding your consciousness is an ongoing process. Be gentle and compassionate with yourself and recognize that self-discovery is a continuous journey.

"The key to growth is the introduction of higher dimensions of consciousness into our awareness."

- Lao Tzu   (Lao Tzu Quotes. n.d.)

States of Consciousness

Varied cognitive states of consciousness reflect your level of awareness, perception, and responsiveness to stimuli.

Normal Wakefulness:

This is the state of being fully awake and aware of your surroundings, thoughts, and sensations. It's the state most people experience during their daily activities.

Sleep:

Sleep is a regular, natural occurrence defined by decreased awareness and sensitivity to the environment. It is vital for refreshment, revitalization, and optimal cognitive functioning.

Dreaming:

This state occurs during the Rapid Eye Movement stage of the sleep cycle. Dreams are vivid, sensory experiences that often involve narratives or scenarios.

Hypnagogia:

This is the state in-between sleep and alertness, often characterized by vivid and sometimes hallucinatory experiences.

Meditative:

This state is characterized by focused attention, relaxation, and a heightened sense of awareness.

Drug-Induced States:

The consumption of mind-altering substances can evoke an altered consciousness, ranging from euphoria to hallucinations, depending on the substance.

Altered States through Trauma or Extreme Stress:

Severe trauma or extreme stress can lead to dissociative states, where people feel disconnected from their sense of self or reality (Rothschild, 2000).

Different states can be associated with different brainwaves.

Brainwaves and Consciousness

As we learned from the gray and white matter section, electrical activity allows the brain to "talk" to itself. Your brain's neurons interact creating measurable electrical patterns referred to as brain waves. Brainwaves are measured using an electroencephalogram machine or EEG with electrodes placed on the scalp. The frequency of brainwaves is denoted in Hertz (Hz), indicating the number of electrical cycles or waves produced by the brain. For instance, 1 Hz signifies one cycle per second.

Each state of consciousness is usually linked to a distinct range of brainwave frequencies. This implies that your brainwaves' frequency (Hz) fluctuates depending on your current activity or mental state.

There are five types of brainwaves, each associated with a different state of consciousness. Your body's physiology mirrors the various states of consciousness as shown below.

Types of brain waves and associated frequency ranges

Gamma waves (30-100 Hz) - Associated with heightened perception and learning during times of high focus and concentration.

Beta waves (12-30 Hz) – Associated with alertness during an active conversation, engaged thinking, and problem-solving during a wakeful state.

Alpha waves (8-12 Hz) - Associated with reflection, creativity, or meditation. A relaxed daydreaming type awareness or calm wakeful state.

Theta waves (4-8 Hz) - Associated with being in a light sleep or using your intuition and accessing your subconscious mind. This can occur during deep relaxation, dreaming, or visualization.

Delta waves (.05-4 Hz) - Associated with a deep, dreamless sleep in an unconscious state. This is what's needed for regenerative sleep and healing
(Why Breathwork Is so Powerful and How to Do It, 2021)

You can influence your brain waves through training. Techniques like meditation, breathwork, grounding exercises, listening to binaural beats, and utilizing brain training apps are effective. This training can enhance your focus, reduce stress, aid creativity, boost memory, regulate emotions, and enrich your meditation practice, leading to spiritual insights and a enriched sense of belonging (Ramdinmawii & Mittal, 2017). Your brainwaves are incredibly important to your Somatic Therapy. You can learn more about your brainwave patterns by consulting an EEG biofeedback therapist, as detailed in Chapter 2.

With everything we have covered so far, you can see that a breathwork and grounding routine impact your body, brain, and consciousness. Let's have a closer look at these simple yet life-changing concepts.

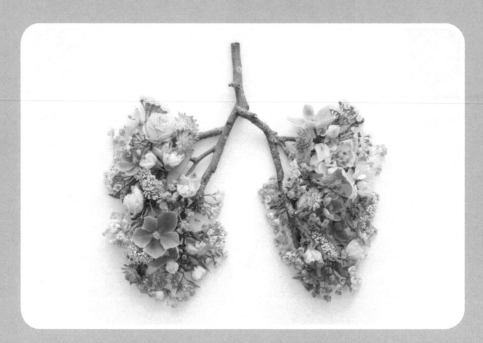

Chapter 5: Closer Look at Breathwork and Grounding/Centering Techniques

What to expect in this chapter:

Breathwork
Grounding and Centering
Scientific research results
Personal experience with Transcendental Meditation
Challenges and Obstacles with Breathwork and Grounding
How to thrive even in the most raging conditions

Own your Breathwork

I quickly learned that my breath was one of my most indispensable aspects. I began my journey to healing by integrating breathwork and grounding/centering techniques into my daily routine. This fusion forms a potent and impactful ritual to help you bond to your body, mind, and soul. It will enrich your wholeness and well-being like nothing else can.

In this chapter, we'll cover breathwork, which calls for the conscious and intentional manipulation of your breath to influence your physical and mental state by awakening your awareness. Focusing on deep, controlled breathing patterns can reduce stress and enhance feelings of relaxation throughout your body (Zaccaro et al., 2018). This is a potent tool that can be utilized almost anytime and anywhere, allowing you to reset your autonomic nervous system, boost your brain's oxygen supply, and lower the carbon dioxide in your blood on demand (Choosing Therapy, 2023). Learning these techniques can be helpful when dealing with high levels of pain, stress, anger, anxiety/panic attacks, and more.

This is an all-natural healing power.

You were created with the ability to literally "Catch your breath" and find balance in your life. The significance of breathwork cannot be understated.

Additionally, we'll explore techniques for grounding and centering. These practices share the common goal of anchoring you in the present and giving you a feeling of calm. Grounding is focused on your physical connection and feeling of stability within. Imagine a tree grounded deeply into Mother Earth; its roots need to anchor into the soil to find balance and not fall over. Like that, catching your breath helps you ground your energy while focusing on your emotional and mental balance.

Let's start with the first part of this one-two punch: breathwork.

"All things share the same breath - the beast, the tree, the man... the air shares its spirit with all the life it supports."

- Chief Seattle   (Chief Seattle Quotes. n.d.)

Understanding breathwork

Exploring the bond between your breath pattern, emotional state, and life is fascinating. Consider this; what is the first thing you did when you came into this world?

What will be the last?

You take a breath!

Your breath is life.

For the remainder of your days, it will support you.

And when you pay attention, it will help restore your balance.

First, your breath acts as a passageway between the mind and body.

It becomes the anchor that allows you to stay grounded in the present moment, serving as a focal point. It keeps you in touch with yourself and your surroundings.

Second, it has a far-reaching impact on your nervous system. Through intentional breathing, you can activate your body's relaxation response also known as the parasympathetic response (Choosing Therapy, 2023). This will allow you to willfully shift your nervous system's operation from fight-flight or freeze mode to a calm state throughout your body and mind

(Gibbons, 2019). It also has other benefits, such as helping to amplify your immune system.

Next, it expedites the release and processing of emotions. As you know, emotions are not solely experienced in the mind but also expressed and felt in the body. Trauma can become imprinted in your body, manifesting as physical tension, constriction, or even mind-body disconnection. Practicing a regular breathwork routine will create a safe container for emotions to surface and be acknowledged. This is why breathwork is often used to work through trauma patterns. The rhythmic and intentional nature of the practice can help you access and release these stored feelings, allowing for emotional healing. Breathwork can help remove the emotional blockages of trauma and start the processing of these suppressed emotions (Ingraham, 2023).

During a breathwork session, you may feel sensations such as heating up prickling, stiffness, pulsating, chilling, or in various body parts. There's a chance you could notice colors and images or have an "aha" moment of clarity as well.

Breathwork has also been proven to increase your brainwaves, as discussed in Chapter 4. Neuroscientists have made a direct correlation between your brainwaves and breathwork. It's proven a successful pathway to guide your brainwaves through the spectrum, starting from beta and smoothly progressing to alpha and even theta frequencies(Choosing Therapy, 2023). Additionally, it has the potential to alleviate your negative thought patterns, reduce stress, and serve as a natural antidepressant (How to Manipulate Brain Waves for a

Better Mental State | Jefferson Health, n.d.).

Sounds too good to be true, right?!

I was skeptical until I began incorporating this transformative practice into my life. The article "Effect of breathwork on stress and mental health: A meta-analysis of randomized-controlled trials" looked at the therapeutic potential of breathing techniques to improve mental health.

Examining 12 trials encompassing 785 adults, research scrutinized stress and depression levels. Results demonstrated a notable reduction in stress among those who practiced breathwork when weighed against the control group that did not. Breathwork positively impacts heart rate variability and is connected to a lesser risk of heart disease (Müller et al., 2017). It directly affects your somatic state by lowering heart rate, stabilizing blood pressure, and optimizing oxygen intake. These findings highlight the impactful role that conscious breathing plays in harmonizing your mind and body. (Fincham, Strauss, Montero-Marín, et al., 2023)

Breathwork is often integrated with other body-based interventions such as movement, touch, and grounding exercises. I enourage you to engage in this practice under the guidance of a trained professional when working with traumas or deep emotional pains.

Let's try observing your inhalation and exhalation pattern now. You will find that your breath will mirror your current inner landscape.

For example, when you're happy, your breathing patterns may look like the following:

Deeper Breaths: Happiness often leads to slower, deeper breaths. This allows for better oxygen exchange in the lungs and can promote a sense of relaxation.

Regular Rhythm: Happy emotions tend to be associated with a more regular and consistent breathing pattern. Your inhales and exhales are likely to be smooth and even.

Diaphragmatic Breathing: **When you're happy, you're more likely to engage your diaphragm, which allows for a fuller, more efficient breath. This can promote a feeling of peace and contentment.**

Relaxed Chest and Shoulders: **Happy breathing often involves minimal tension in the chest and shoulder area. Instead, you might feel more expansion in your abdomen as you breathe.**

On the other hand, when you're upset, your breathing pattern tends to change in several noticeable ways:

Shallow Breaths: **Upset emotions can lead to more shallow breathing. This means you might get insufficient oxygen compared to your body's needs. This can contribute to your feelings of tension or anxiety (Ingraham, 2023).**

Rapid Breathing: **Emotional upset can trigger a faster breathing rate. This is often associated with the body's "fight-fight" response.**

Chest Dominance: **When upset, you may find that your breath is concentrated more in your chest, with less diaphragm engagement. This can create a feeling of tightness or constriction (Choosing Therapy, 2023).**

Irregular Rhythm: **Emotional distress can cause irregular breathing patterns. You might experience sudden inhales, exhales, or pauses in your breath.**

Remember these considerations when observing your breathing patterns; they can signal when it's time to regulate your emotional state. By focusing on having this on your breathing patterns, you are gaining awareness of your being.

Breathwork is a powerful method established in ancient traditions from all around the globe (Ashton, 2022). Proving that our ancestors knew of the many benefits of breathwork. There are hundreds of techniques and styles, each with its emphasis and intention.

Here is a brief introduction to various breathwork methods you may wish to explore further or discuss with your therapist.

g-tummo breathing or Vase breathing:

This Tibetan tradition combines breathing and visualization, aka using mental imagery, to energize your mind and body. Vase refers to your lower belly protruding or taking a vase or pot shape when you contract your abdominal and pelvic muscles.

It is known to increase alpha, beta, and gamma brain waves. This will initiate your Sympathetic Nervous System, increasing your heart rate, blood pressure, cognitive capacity, and mental clarity. This is a great way to reach deeper states of meditation.

Conscious connected technique:

This is an excellent approach to discovering the full capabilities of your respiratory system. With this technique, you take full, deep breaths without pausing. It involves a circular breathing pattern where you exhale as soon as you reach the top of the inhale. Then, before finishing the exhalation, you inhale again, linking one breath to the other.

This is done laying down in a relaxing position, with the jaw at ease and mouth wide open. This technique can help expand and grow your consciousness and let go of old thought patterns. This approach promotes emotional and physical release and increases mental clarity, all attributed to improved brain oxygenation. Consult a trained practitioner, as this technique can bring up deep trauma.

Coherent frequency breathing:

This method involves controlling the rate and depth of your breathing to align with your body's natural rhythm. For instance, you might inhale gradually for a count of five, hold your breath for a count of five, and subsequently exhale for a count of five. Duplicate this pattern for several minutes, steadily expanding the count to six or seven when comfortable. Focusing on your breath's rhythm and keeping your mind from wandering is important. This technique can help with pain management, stress reduction, heart health, and sleep quality.

Belly or Deep Diaphragmatic breathing:

The aim of this approach is to guide you use the diaphragm properly while breathing. Find a calm place to sit or lay. Shut your eyes and ease your muscles.

Position your hand on your abdomen and concentrate on deep breaths. Inhale gradually through your nostrils, enabling your belly to rise, then exhale softly through your mouth, allowing your stomach to contract. Pay attention to the breath's sensation; if your abdomen presses against your hand, you're engaging your diaphragm. This technique can help improve your mood, digestion, oxygen intake, and lower blood pressure.

Box or square breathing:

This simple and powerful technique can help quickly bring you down from somatic or emotional arousal. This method involves systematic counting, inhalation, breath retention, exhalation, and another pause, all in equal segments. Find a comfortable seated position and gently shut your eyes

Breathe in deeply through your nasal passages, counting to four, and feel your stomach expanding.

Breathe in slowly through your nose, counting to four

Hold your breath, counting to four slowly.

Empty your lungs by breathing out slowly through your mouth, counting to four

Pause and hold your breath for four beats before moving on to the next cycle.

Practice this routine for a few minutes, keeping a consistent pace.

The act of counting can instantly divert your minds attention from whatever is stressing you. This is a mighty weapon against the fight-flight response (Why Breathwork Is so Powerful and How to Do It, 2021).

Breath of Fire:

This approach involves rapid, forceful, rhythmic exhales and relaxed inhales with a closed mouth. It can guide you to decreased stress, increased energy, and better lung function and concentration (Choosing Therapy, 2023). This method can help regulate your pituitary gland, which involves the release of hormones and homeostasis. Consult a professional therapist concerning this technique, especially if you are pregnant or have heart, spinal, or breathing issues.

Alternate nostril breathing:

This yoga breathing method requires inhaling and exhaling through a single nostril at a time, while your fingers seal the other nostril Choosing Therapy, 2023). You can alter your nervous system by breathing through just one nostril. The right nostril corresponds to sympathetic activation, while the left is linked to parasympathetic activation. This approach can reduce stress and blood pressure while boosting your memory (Pal et al., 2014). This technique can help stimulate the Vagus Nerve and regulate the amygdala section of the brain, which is in charge of your emotional responses.

Kapalabhati:

This is a phenomenal practice to warm up before meditation or before exercising. It could support your heart and lung health.

It involves short, rapid, and forceful exhalations followed by relaxed inhalations through the nose in cycles of 1-2 exhales per second. It could energize the body, clear your mind, and improve focus (Malhotra et al., 2022).

Wim Hof Method:

Devised by Wim Hof, this method could offer a promising route for alleviating depression, managing pain, addressing Fibromyalgia, and mitigating migraines. It combines a specific breathing pattern of deep breaths held as long as you can, cold exposure, and various mindset techniques.

Exposing yourself to cold will activate your stress response. Think of it as a practical training boot camp for your future stress management. It will decrease cortisol, boost your immune system, improve your circulation, and release good mood endorphins. Over time, you can learn to embrace the cold exposure with meditation via an ice bath or cold shower. Start with small increments of exposure time. There is even a study that suggests this could be an excellent way to clear waste built up in the brain. (Innerfire, 2023)

No matter which technique you and your therapist select, the main goal is to optimize and open up your breath Expanding your breath means improving your lung capacity and increasing oxygen flow in your body. There are countless ways that a breathwork routine can improve your life.

It's time to incorporate these breathing techniques into your daily life

You can jump right in with a variety of purposeful breath exercises. Integrating them into your everyday routine is crucial, starting from today. You can begin by setting reminders or using specific cues, like when you open a door, receive a text notification, or take a sip of water, to prompt a moment of focused breathing.

Another approach is to set aside dedicated times throughout the day for brief breathing exercises, such as a few minutes upon waking, before meals, or during breaks. Integrating conscious breathing with routine activities like walking, cooking, or commuting can infuse mindfulness into your daily tasks.

If you think about it, it is so easy.

You can do it nearly anywhere, nearly anytime.

Consider creating a dedicated space for breathing exercises within your home. This space can be a peaceful haven for your purposeful breathwork—a sanctuary devoted to your healing journey.

"When someone is properly grounded in life, they shouldn't have to look outside themselves for approval."
-Epictetus   (Epictetus Quotes. n.d.)

Understanding Grounding

Grounding involves reconnecting your physical body with the physical world and the present moment. Think of the grounded tree I mentioned earlier. Grounding may also be referred to as earthing. Earthing involves connecting to the Earth's organic electrical charge to stabilize your body's physiology at its core (Chevalier et al., 2013). This practice can decrease inflammation, alleviate pain and stress, and enhance your blood circulation, energy levels, and sleep quality. Another remarkable aspect is that these positive effects can take place quickly.

Research has shown that grounding the body has wide-ranging and significant physiological benefits, as evidenced by nearly 20 studies to date. In addition to the electrical charge, grounding techniques focus on recognizing your bodily sensations and data from all of your senses, promoting total body awareness. This can be achieved through body scans or mindful movement exercises from Chapter 3. These techniques will contribute to a better sense of internal safety and connection to reality.

It is an intentional pursuit of anchoring yourself when everything around you is moving. Grounding practices comprise extensive activities such as breath control, mindfulness, body scanning, affirmations, and even yoga. It could involve focused time in nature or even just mindfully sitting under a tree. These practices will allow you to redirect your attention from racing thoughts or overwhelming emotions toward the sensations in your body and the immediate environment.

You can find stability, harmony, and a feeling of rootedness by grounding yourself. Rootedness refers to the state of being deeply attached to the present moment. Being "rooted" means having a sense of emotional balance, self-assurance, and resilience. A sense of rootedness aids your ability to make decisions with clarity and a focused mind. It cultivates the confidence necessary to navigate times of stress and anxiety with composure.

Grounding will aid you in keeping your composure by adding a greater sense of calm. By encouraging a sense of embodiment and presence, grounding practices contribute to your emotional regulation, strength, and contentment in life.

The connection you will feel to the environment around you and the present moment will boost your sense of belonging in the universe. Many people pray regularly for this very same connection. This link was the element I didn't realize was absent until I discovered it. Grounding exercises will help regulate your emotions, reduce anxiety, and renew stability in your life when things become overwhelming.

Grounding and your emotional state are intimately connected. Grounding practices have the power to regulate and influence your emotional vitality. Grounding techniques will bring you out of your head and into your body, allowing you to connect with your physical sensations and immediately interrupt your negative thought patterns.

One powerful grounding practice to consider is visualization with affirmations. This involves fusing creative thinking with optimistic declarations to create your desired reality. By picturing goals clearly and constantly while affirming your capabilities, you can bolster your motivation and confidence in achieving success. This increased confidence will make your goals more likely to come true. For example, shut your eyes and picture being a giant tree with roots stretching far into the Earth. Visualize these roots, grounding you and providing stability. While visualizing this, you could tell yourself, "I am unshakable, my roots run deep, and I'm absolutely where I want to be." You can change the statement to whatever you want based on your intention and needs at that moment.

Understanding Centering

Centering is the process of bringing your thoughts, energy, and emotions to a calm and "centered" state. Being "centered" refers to feeling a sense of inner balance, calmness, and focus. It's where you feel emotionally stable and clear-headed even when facing stress. This feeling allows you to better manage your emotions and thoughts without being as quickly bothered by others or stressful situations. You can be the "calm in the storm" instead of being the storm. Through centering, your actions and reactions will originate from a place rooted in deeper understanding and empathy.

You should add moments of centering to your daily routine. This can be achieved through breathwork, meditation, and affirmations, to name a few. You may experience stress, anxiety, or sadness as you go about your day. Addressing this promptly is crucial. Consider taking a moment, maybe during a break or before bedtime, to process these emotions daily. Be present momentarily with the feelings to stay in control and settle yourself before it becomes a more significant emotional or physical health issue. Without centering as part of your life, you will leave the feelings of stress or anxiety trapped in your body. This routine doesn't aim to simply make your feelings vanish. Instead, it's designed to heighten your awareness of what you feel so that you can manage your responses more effectively. It will help you make decisions about the stressor, anxiety, or sadness mindfully and from a place of wisdom. Centering is how you can increase your confidence and be your true, authentic self, not controlled by your triggers. (Christian, 2023)

It puts you in the emotional driver's seat.

Breathwork and grounding/centering form the most powerful synergy for natural healing.

It's time to work these grounding/centering techniques into your daily life.

As with the breathwork exercises, you can start grounding/centering techniques today. Start by engaging with nature and using all of your senses; it's such an immersive experience. I recommend that you actively participate in everything nature offers to the best of your physical capabilities. Try tuning into the soft flutter of leaves, the melody of birds singing, the earthy fragrance after a rainfall, the sweet embrace of a cool breeze, and the touch of grass beneath your feet. It will awaken your connection to the universe around you. Try immersing yourself in nature; you will tap into a major source of healing. You will rekindle a feeling of amazement with the Earth. You will appreciate the things we sometimes take for granted around us. It will revitalize your spirit, and you will gain a profound appreciation for the beauty instead of the beast that the world can sometimes seem.

You can take a couple of moments daily to reflect, pray, or just sit in a quiet space to think about your feelings. Yes, I know many of you have never meditated, and it can be an intimidating word. Many believe they simply can't "shut" their brains off, and it's not about shutting it off. It's about tuning it in.

ANYONE can meditate with effort, time, and practice. If you really "can't" relax, then meditation is exactly what you need. It all starts with being mindfully present and focused on your breath. Start by focusing your thoughts toward your breathing. Concentrate only on the present moment. Limit your distractions so that you can start with the following exercises or the mindfulness and breathing exercises from previous chapters.

For both grounding and centering, it's essential to be aware of your mood and allow a moment to reflect when you feel off balance.

Ready to try?

Grounding through the feet:

Find a comfortable standing position, barefoot if possible, and bring your attention to your feet. Slowly shift your weight from one foot to the other, feeling the connection between your feet and the ground. Notice the sensations in the soles of your feet—the pressure, temperature, and texture.

Take deep, mindful breaths as you connect with the surface beneath you. This exercise promotes body awareness and a sense of stability. It can be practiced for a few minutes daily and will help develop a more profound link to your physical being.

Get a grounding object:

Keep a small object with you that has a comforting or

"grounding" significance, such as a smooth stone, a worry stone, your favorite crystal, ring or bracelet.

When you feel like overburdened or disconnected, grip the item in your hand and fix your focus on the way the surface feels, the heaviness, or any other sensory qualities. This can acts as a reminder to be present and grounded.

Progressive Muscle Relaxation:

Mentally scan your body, beginning with your feet, flexing and then releasing each muscle group throughout your body, moving upward. This exercise will help release muscle tension and help you work on your present-moment awareness and relaxation.

Grounding through Music!

Listening to calming or "grounding" music is really beneficial (Ramdinmawii & Mittal, 2017). Pay attention to the melodies and beat. Allow the music to guide your focus and help you feel centered with less anxiety (Wiwatwongwana et al., 2016). I sometimes use "focus" music to lend a hand in my grounding. I sit in a quiet room with over-the-ear headphones, listening to Binaural Beats or ADHD relief music online.

Interested in binaural music?

Binaural music is a recording and reproduction technique designed to craft a three-dimensional sound experience. This is achieved by strategically placing two microphones (or speakers) to mimic the spatial qualities of human ears, capturing sound from various directions. Listening to binaural audio through headphones generates an immersive and lifelike auditory environment, creating the sensation of actually being in the recorded space. This allows your brain to seamlessly connect with the music, guiding you into a serene and focused state (Mazziotta et al., 1982). It's particularly beneficial for people with ADHD or those who are neurodivergent. Check out the Naty H.E.A.L.S. YouTube channel for examples.

Five Senses Exercise:

This involves focusing on the five senses, mindfully observing and describing sensory stimuli in the present moment. It could help create new neural connections and improve your present-moment awareness. To complete this exercise, you will name five items within your sight, four things you can touch, three things can make sound, two things with a scent, and one thing with flavor you can try within your presence. This exercise is excellent for connecting your mind to the present and grounding you in your surroundings.

Visualize a safe place:

Shut your eyes and imagine a location where you are completely secure, calm, and at peace. Go through as many details of the space as you can. Think about how it appears, looks, feels, and any sounds you hear. Linger in this space until you sense greater balance and tranquility.

A fun variation of this involves art therapy - safe place collage:

Gather images from magazines or other sources representing a safe and calming environment. Arrange and glue these images onto a piece of paper or poster board, creating a visual representation of your personal safe space. This exercise will empower you to harness your imagination and explore feelings of safety and security. You will create a tangible reminder of where you can find solace and relaxation.

Visualize your energy:

Shut your eyes and see in your mind's eye, a tiny luminous orb or energy glowing in the middle of your chest, then imagine this ball growing and expanding enough to fill your entire body with warmth and peace.

Journaling:

As you learned from the self-reflection activities in Chapter 3, journaling is a centering superstar. This is an excellent way to start understanding your thoughts, feelings, stress, and anxieties to center and move forward in life. Often, people with untreated stress, anxiety, and trauma have fatigue or low energy. This is because the act of not letting go of the pain, fear, guilt, and worry takes an immense amount of energy from your body. Journaling is one of the most effective methods of letting go and energizing your body and life. Use your journaling time to center and let go of your attachment with past and fears of the future (Gortner et al., 2006).

Devoting just a few minutes daily to these activities is a small investment for the valuable results you deserve.

Scientific research on grounding/centering

It has been proven that during and after meditation, there were changes in somatic and psychological measures simultaneously (Travis, 2012). One such study was discussed in the article "Autonomic and EEG Patterns Distinguish Transcending from Other Experiences During Transcendental Meditation Practice" The study was about the practice of Transcendental Meditation or TM. This is a specific silent meditation technique founded by Maharishi Mahesh Yogi. It involves sitting comfortably and silently repeating a mantra to facilitate the settling of the mind into complete relaxation, inner stillness, and expanded awareness. The mantra is given to students by trained a fully Transcendental Meditation teacher. The study looked at 90 school administrators before and after learning TM within 3 months. The study aimed to correlate specific meditation experiences with various somatic measures. This study compared EEG and other autonomic patterns when transcending during TM practice. (Travis, 2001)

Transcendence involves entering a heightened state of consciousness beyond your normal state. This means there is a stillness, pure awareness, and great calm within you.

The acronym EEG refers to Electroencephalography, which is a method to detect bio-signals in the brain, as discussed in Chapter 4. The test subjects would meditate, and a bell would ring three times during the meditation. The subject's EEG and other states were measured around each bell ring.

The results are amazing...they proved that meditation alone can create the following:

- Lower breath rate

- Higher respiratory sinus arrhythmia amplitudes

- Higher EEG alpha brainwave strength

- Higher alpha coherence

What could this look like to you?

Lower breath rate:

A lower breath rate typically indicates a slower and more relaxed breathing pattern. This can help induce a state of calmness and relaxation in the body and mind. It could reduce stress, decrease blood pressure, and promote overall harmony.

Higher respiratory sinus arrhythmia (RSA) amplitudes:

Respiratory sinus arrhythmia means the built-in organic fluctuation in heart rate that occurs with each breath. Higher RSA amplitudes indicate a more prominent variation in heart rate during respiration. Usually, this is recognized as a positive marker for your cardiovascular well-being and reflects a healthy autonomic nervous system. This promotes your total cardiovascular efficiency and strength.

Higher EEG alpha brainwave strength:

EEG alpha waves are associated with a relaxed, calm, and wakeful state of consciousness. Higher alpha amplitudes indicate a greater prevalence of alpha waves in the brain, suggesting a deeper state of relaxation, reduced mental chatter and increased mental clarity. It may contribute to improved focus, creativity, and a sense of contentment.

Higher alpha coherence:

Alpha coherence refers to the synchronization and connectivity of alpha waves between different brain regions. Higher alpha coherence indicates a more harmonious communication between brain regions associated with alpha activity. This coherence may boost your cognitive processing, memory, and overall brain functioning.

But that's not all.

The study also found that brain integration was significantly higher, meaning that the integration of the brain waves seen during transcending was substantially greater than the control group. Brain integration refers to the harmonious coordination and communication between different brain regions. It involves the efficient exchange of information and synchronization of neural activity. This could look like enhanced thought processing, emotional regulation, and general cognitive balance. Brain integration is associated with optimal brain health and performance. They also found that bell rings induced a stronger skin conductance reaction during transcendence. Skin conductance, or galvanic skin response, measures the skin's electrical conductivity. It reflects changes in sweat gland activity, influenced by emotional arousal and stress. Skin conductance often indicates Sympathetic Nervous System activity and emotional reactivity. As a result of experiencing TM, the subjects experienced decreases in negative psychological states, decreases in anxiety, anger, depression, fatigue, confusion, and an increase in overall vigor.

Quite impressive if you ask me!

My results

Discovering the transformative power of TM: it's not just a practice; it's my sanctuary. Overcoming chronic pain and mental illness, I found solace in the stillness, embracing the calm within the chaos of my mind and body. Meditation taught me to be present, to breathe, to heal, and to connect to my consciousness. In its quietude, I found my strength. As you now know, I've suffered for a long time with Fibromyalgia, Bipolar, PTSD, addiction to prescription meds, depression, anxiety, and other challenges for many years, followed by a fractured spine.

Before adopting Transcendental Meditation, or TM, I grappled intensely with both mental and physical pain. While I successfully maintained sobriety through alternative grounding and meditation techniques, the chronic pain persisted. Since adding TM to my life, I've experienced valuable changes in my somatic and psychological measures. I noticed decreases in my negative emotional state along with reduced anxiety and anger. I am much happier, can focus better, and can deal with tricky situations better. What I am most grateful for is the ability to mentally deal with the physical pain better than ever. As a mother, wife, lifelong student, patient, and human, I often face stressful situations. The symptoms of Fibromyalgia intensify my pain during stressful moments, so experiencing less stress has significantly alleviated my pain. In my view, starting with breathwork and grounding should be your initial step toward healing.

Potential challenges and obstacles with breathwork and grounding/centering:

Some potential challenges with breathwork include physical discomfort or racing thoughts (Choosing Therapy, 2023). This is normal to deal with when you first begin your practice. Many people give up because they believe they are not doing it properly. However, I encourage you to think of your racing thoughts as your brain letting off steam. Acknowledge the thoughts, write them down if necessary, and then return to your practice. If you encounter this and it's too much, consider modifying your breathing techniques or consult a professional for guidance to stay on course.

There may be occasional difficulties with grounding/centering arising from distractions or restlessness. You are moving energy throughout your body & healing; it's expected to need rest after a session to allow your body to catch up. If you encounter this, consider beginning with shorter sessions initially. This might make it simpler to maintain focus.

Alternatively, you can explore using online guided grounding/centering exercises.

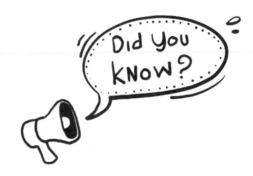

Technology Overload: The pervasive use of technology contributes to mind-body disconnection. A survey by the Pew Research Center found that around 93% of grown-ups in the United States own a cell phone, and excessive screen time can lead to disengagement from physical sensations and a reduced awareness of the present moment.

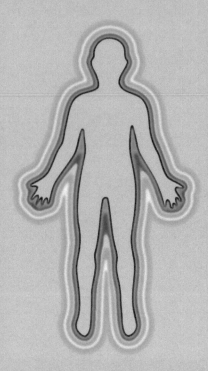

Chapter 6:
Closer Look at Movement and Body-Oriented Techniques

> "It's not what happens to you, but how you react to it that matters."
> – Epictetus   (Epictetus Quotes. n.d.)

Talk less – Heal More

Somatic movement and body-centered methods offer a holistic approach to healing. Movement techniques emphasize bodily motions and expression, while body-centered approaches prioritize touch and physical sensations. Both ways excel in trauma therapy and are great for those struggling to talk about their emotions or who have body image concerns. The intention is to gain a deeper connection with your body (Bloch-Atefi & Ja, 2015).

Understanding movement techniques

Movement techniques involve purposeful actions that help you tune into your bodily sensations, such as your posture, flexibility, muscle tension, balance, Qi flow, and sensations like pleasure, pain, tingling, pulsing, or numbness. Techniques include dance therapy, yoga, and the Feldenkrais method from Chapter 2.

With your physical participation, you will release tension, enhance your mood, reduce stress, build confidence, and streamline your emotional healing. Engaging in these techniques will create a meaningful dialogue between your mind and body, particularly your muscles and joints. It's ideal if you are looking to boost your range of motion, particularly if you experience muscle stiffness (Kiepe et al., 2012). The key is approaching these methods with curiosity, patience, and non-judgment. Allow your body to guide you and honor the messages it sends in return. These techniques offer a space to truly relish the liberating power of self-expression we all yearn for.

Specific movements and postures directly impact your mental state by influencing and regulating your emotions. Think about how you feel standing tall with an open chest and relaxed shoulders; this is your confidence. I almost feel like a superhero. Yet, while slouching or hunching, you can feel heavier, more sadness or low energy, and off-balanced. The simple act of consciously adjusting your body posture can influence your emotional experiences right now.

Movement techniques provide a gateway for emotional manifestation and release. They have a meaningful impact on your emotional vitality. This means your ability to express a wide range of emotions in a balanced way, allowing them to flow freely through your body. This process could lead to a sense of catharsis or open the release valve for your much-needed emotional venting.

Catharsis refers to releasing or purging strong emotions,

particularly through artistic or expressive means. It is a process of emotional or mental detoxifying. This is great for all of the suppressed or repressed emotions that you need to get rid of.

Catharsis provides a sense of relief that will allow you to experience and express feelings such as fear, sadness, anger, or grief safely and constructively. All of this can be accomplished without the need for verbal communication. I'm talking about diving deep, reflecting on the entire story, and letting it hit you. It's all about going through the emotion. It may seem silly; however, letting out a scream into a pillow or a socially acceptable place can be an excellent way to process your feelings. This can be incredibly cathartic. Simply let out your thoughts, frustrations, or whatever is on your mind until you've released it all into the universe. This sense of emotional release can provide "resolution" followed by personal growth. Resolution refers to having a sense of closure, relief, or clarity about the trauma or emotions. It can be a transformative experience that smooths the path of your healing and self-understanding.

As you know, your body holds the physical manifestations of emotional experiences. Chronic tension or pain in some regions of the body may be an sign of unresolved emotional issues. If this applies to you, I recommend trying movement techniques as soon as possible.

Examples of movement techniques you can explore

Yoga:

A practice rooted in antiquity, it combines body poses, intentional breath control, and meditation to promote maneuverability, physical power, better sleep, immune and respiratory function, self-awareness, Qi flow, pain relief, mental clarity, and stress reduction, to name a few. Qi, aka Chi, is the life force that provides energy for the body to function (Zhang & Rose, 2001). Qi flows along meridian pathways. These pathways are non-physical passageways within your body that the qi travels. It is used to aid your body's self-healing process and ease pain (Yadav et al., 2012).

Alexander Technique®:

The goal is to enhance your posture, coordination, and balance by retraining your ingrained movement patterns. The treatment addresses potential misalignments causing discomfort, particularly on head, neck, and spine movements (MacPherson et al., 2015). Sessions are usually conducted one-on-one, where you'll perform specific movements to assess your unique patterns. This is good for those with chronic and back pain, stress, poor posture, repetitive stress injuries, anxiety, Parkinson's disease, TMJ, and voice disorders, to name a few (Little et al., 2008). Search online for the professional directory for local practitioners of this technique. It's exclusively instructed by individuals who've undergone a rigorous three-year certification process and possess at least a bachelor's degree.

Pilates®:

Emphasizes the vitality of your core, joint fluidity, and coordination through controlled motions and focused breaths. This could benefit those experiencing neck or shoulder tension, joint issues, poor posture, chronic pain, stress, and anxiety, as well as those who are pregnant or have osteoporosis, to name a few. If you prefer low-impact exercise, this is a great option. Both group and private classes are available. Pilates® practice is possible with only a mat; most classes incorporate specialized equipment.

Tai Chi:

This traditional Chinese martial art emphasizes relaxation, balance, and the circulation of Qi through deliberate, graceful movements. Fit for everyone, regardless of age and fitness level, it offers a relaxed form of exercise. This low-impact routine reduces stress, enhancing flexibility and range of motion. Options include online, group classes, or private instruction.

Trager Psychophysical Integration aka Trager Approach®:

This approach, designed and registered by Milton Trager, involves rhythmic, gentle movements and touch to promote deep emotional relaxation, release body tension, and improve mobility. You would learn simple movements that could induce a soothing sensation and unburdened feeling all over. The aim is for you to master efficient, effortless motion. In a 90-minute private session with a certified Trager® practitioner®, you can address issues such as back, neck, and joint pain.

This list is not exhaustive; there are numerous other movement techniques for you to discover.

Scientific research on movement techniques

When we engage in physical movements, such as exercise, yoga, or dance, our body releases endorphins and other neurotransmitters to enhance mood and reduce stress (Yadav et al., 2012). It has been shown that these "feel-good" chemicals boost your sense of contentment and could lessen the signs of unease and depression. A study involving 86 participants, split into 44 females and 42 males, demonstrated that adopting a brief 10-day yoga routine was linked to a decrease in stress indicators and inflammation. (Yadav et al., 2012).

Understanding body-oriented techniques

Body-oriented techniques can include touch, breathwork, and exercises designed to heighten your body awareness (Bloch-Atefi & Ja, 2015). Their objective is to aid in the release of physical tension and trauma (Barratt, 2013). Chapter 2 introduced 15 core Somatic Therapy techniques. Now, we'll delve deeper into one of them—Somatic Experiencing® (SE)—to offer a more detailed understanding of these approaches.

Somatic Experiencing® (SE): Dr. Peter A. Levine pioneered an approach centered on trauma resolution through an attentive focus on your bodily sensations. It was designed to aid in the self-regulation of your nervous system. The two fundamental SE® concepts are titration and pendulation. The term titration comes from chemistry, which refers to the controlled addition of a substance to a solution (Levine, 2010). Similarly, in Somatic Therapy, titration involves approaching overwhelming experiences or sensations step-by-step. This will gradually increase your capacity to process any traumatic experiences. During a session, you work with small increments of intensity to avoid overwhelming your nervous system. Instead of diving straight into the most intense aspects of the trauma, the therapist will help you explore your body's responses in manageable doses. This gradual approach helps to prevent re-traumatization and allows the nervous system to cope with distressing circumstances in a safe and regulated manner (GoodTherapy Editor Team, 2018b).

It's a very cautious and gradual exploration that is managed for you.

Titration includes the gentle examination of small segments of sensations or experiences related to the traumatic event, ensuring it remains within your comfort and tolerance levels (GoodTherapy Editor Team, 2018b). You will focus on the parts that are calm, comfortable, or neutral. Starting with less distressing sensations, you can gradually grow roots of security and trust in your body.

As therapy advances, you and your therapist will jointly pinpoint areas of tension, discomfort, or heightened activation in your body. Once the most intense aspects of the trauma are identified, the therapist will gradually address these areas. You may be asked to observe subtle changes in sensation or explore sensations in short, manageable intervals. This will allow your nervous system to finally process and regulate the experience. Titration also involves a delicate balance between periods of "activation" and "regulation." An activated state is a heightened somatic and psychological arousal level originating from within or outside sources (GoodTherapy Editor Team, 2018b).

As you know, activating the nervous system stimulates the nerves and neurons to send signals throughout your body. The therapist will help you recognize when moving into an activated state. This state may involve increased heart rate, rapid breathing, or feeling intense emotions. In such moments, the therapist will help you return to a state of peace and decompression. This back-and-forth movement between an activated state and a relaxed state is referred to as pendulation. It allows the nervous system to gradually expand its capacity to tolerate and integrate your overwhelming experiences. This is serious whole-body training.

Through this process of titration and pendulation, you could learn to navigate the stress or distressing events in an approach that could improve your quality of life. Your body's natural self-regulatory capacity is restored through this process. Symptoms such as anxiety, hypervigilance, flashbacks, and physical pain could diminish. (GoodTherapy Editor Team, 2018b). While Somatic Experiencing® is a very specific treatment method, it is a great example to showcase the goals and features of all body-oriented techniques.

Examples of other body-oriented techniques you can explore

Somatic Massage Therapy:

This massage therapy emphasizes the mind-body connection by using slow movements to manipulate your soft tissues. It may involve breathing techniques, stretches, and self-awareness practices. The aim is to alleviate muscle tension and knots, improve circulation, and release emotional stress. These sessions are highly effective for trauma recovery, allowing you to undress to a level you feel comfortable with. Additionally, they can be beneficial for those dealing with PTSD or substance abuse. You may have to research to find a qualified therapist locally, but it will be worth it.

Craniosacral Therapy (CST):

This approach, refined in the 1960s, is a gentle, hands-on method that aims to release tension in the Craniosacral system, which includes your bodily fluids, skeletal system, neural pathways, and connective structures of the cranium and spinal zone. In a typical hour-long session, you could lay on a massage table where the therapist would gently hold a part of your body and listen for the flow of cerebrospinal fluids. These fluids protect the central nervous system from trauma, nourish system tissue, and remove waste from the brain. The goal is to stabilize the flow of these fluids. This could be good for headaches, stress, depression, chronic pain, sleep issues, emotional trauma, self-awareness, and circulation, to name a few. You need to find a certified CST provider.

Rolfing®:

This practice, which Dr. Ida P. Rolf developed, is also called Structural Integration®. This technique involves targeted tissue maneuvering and movement education to improve your posture, alignment, and overall well-being. It aims to realign your body's connective tissues for improved movement and balance (Caspari & Massa, 2012). You will usually have 10 sessions at a time. This is a hands-on manipulation to modify your structural alignment. Perfect for those who hold physical stress in the body, causing musculoskeletal pain and stiffness (Brandl et al., 2022). It could also help Fibromyalgia (Stall & Teixeira, 2014). Search for a local Certified Rolfing® practitioner.

Mindfully engaging in movement and body-oriented practices,

you can become more connected and regain balance and internal safety, awakening your inner intelligence. You will be more in touch with your bodily sensations, providing the valuable feedback required for your healing journey. As you can see, connection and awareness are common themes of Somatic Therapy.

I enjoy a good yoga stretch in my morning routine.

Ready to try some movement and body-oriented exercises now?

Mindful Stretching:

Pause for a couple of moments each morning or during the day to purposefully lengthen and expand your body. Tune into the sensations, and gently elongate your muscles while breathing deeply. Gentle stretching or yoga poses can increase your blood flow, promote flexibility, release tension, and bring focused attention to your physical form.

Dance Breaks:

Whenever you feel a surge of energy or need a break, turn on your favorite music and enjoy a short dance session. Let your body move freely and expressively. Dancing releases endorphins, uplifts your mood and rejuvenates your body and mind. Dance or expressive movement will provide an excellent outlet for you to release emotions. You will also tap into creativity and experience feelings of freedom and joy.

Conscious Posture:

Pay attention to your posture throughout the day. Sit or stand tall, align your spine, and relax your shoulders. Notice how your body feels and make changes to preserve correct alignment. This cultivates body awareness, improves posture, and prevents discomfort.

Body Rolling:

Rest on a soft exercise ball or foam roller while completing this workout. Gently glide different body parts across it, beginning with your back and gradually moving to areas like hips, thighs, and shoulders. Be mindful of new feelings, body strains, or discomfort. Let your body ease and unwind as you roll. This technique promotes body awareness and relaxation and helps release muscular tension and stress. Experiment with moving gently, tuning into your body, and adjusting the pressure or intensity as needed. Remember, the key is to approach these practices with a sense of curiosity, non-judgment, and presence. Give yourself permission to let go and have fun. Set aside time for daily practice, and your future self will thank you.

Potential challenges and obstacles

Though physical movement and body-oriented techniques offer various advantages, they may also pose challenges. For those with physical limitations or injuries, fully engaging in certain activities might be challenging. Personalizing exercises based on your body's condition is essential, and consulting with a professional is important before starting any new approach. Those with time constraints or a predominantly sedentary lifestyle may face difficulty incorporating regular physical movement into their routine. Additionally, self-consciousness or discomfort with your body may hinder full engagement.

Rising above these obstacles demands patience, self-compassion, innovative approaches, and establishing a nurturing atmosphere for yourself. Finding creative and fun ways to blend movement into your daily ritual is important. As you flip to the next chapter, you'll embark on a journey to heal the wounds of trauma. Here, you'll navigate through the intricate layers of your life, gently untangling the threads that connect you to your past.

"The best cure for the body is a quiet mind."

- Napoleon Bonaparte Napoleon Bonaparte Quotes. (n.d.).

Chapter 7:
Closer Look at Trauma:
Heal Your Emotional
Wounds

What to expect in this chapter:

Repressed and Suppressed emotions

What happens in the freeze, fight, or flight response?

A dysregulated stress response

Types of traumas

Differences in trauma throughout life

Symptoms of trauma

Types of trauma specific therapies

"The very first part in healing is shattering the silence,"
— Erin Merryn

Understanding the hidden details of trauma

So far, we have covered the various impacts of trauma and stress on your physical and mental welfare. Now, let's delve into more details that pertain specifically to trauma. Numerous factors can play a role in the evolution of signs and conditions stemming from traumatic events (Kajantie & Phillips, 2006). It's crucial to understand that these might not manifest immediately; they could take minutes, days or even years to surface.

Factors that impact the development of symptoms from trauma and stress include

Genetics

A family history of anxiety or PTSD. According to the National Institute of Health, a family history shows the passing down of autism, attention deficit hyperactivity disorder (ADHD), bipolar disorder, major depression, and schizophrenia.

Gender

In the case of PTSD, females tend to have increased rates over males. The presence of anxiety and depression in your mental health history can contribute to symptoms of trauma (Ditlevsen & Elklit, 2010)

Personality Traits

People who are introverted, struggle with emotional regulation, hold a pessimistic outlook on life, or grapple with self-doubt are at risk

History of Trauma

Repeated trauma can lead to a higher risk of future trauma symptoms (BioBeats, 2021)

Level of Exposure

Experiencing an event firsthand versus learning about it, as well as the length and continuance of the experience, can be influential factors

Intensity

Experiencing intense fear for your own life versus the lives of others, whether you were trapped versus escaped quickly, or if you had a significant injury versus a minor one, could all be contributing factors

Perception

One person may view an event as life-threatening, and another may view it as manageable

Access to and use of resources

Your ability and willingness to seek professional help, the sooner you get help, the better

Support network

Your ability and willingness to approach family, friends or community resources

As you know, your emotions and unresolved trauma express your story through a variety of sensations, postures, and even your breath. They communicate within your body via a silent language.

But what is the silent language of trauma?

Your pain points!

Your trauma talks through your emotional distress, physical symptoms, flashbacks, avoidance, tunnel vision, irritability, negative thoughts, distrust, anger, and mind-body disconnection (Rothschild, 2000). If you find yourself experiencing nightmares, avoiding certain thoughts, places, or people linked to the experience, being easily startled or showing signs of aggression, engaging in self-destructive behavior, blaming yourself, feeling a sense of resentment towards the world, becoming emotionally detached or losing interest in once-beloved things or people, or are struggling to express any positive emotions, this is your trauma talking (Gimpl & Fahrenholz, 2001). These pain points act as a protective measure for your self-preservation and emotional defense; however, they only hold you back from long-term healing.

Regarding emotions, we have the option of dealing with them through expression, repression, and suppression. While we've covered expressing emotions, repression and suppression are different approaches.

Repressed emotions deliberately shove distressing memories, images, or emotions from conscious awareness. We do this because we go into a fight-flight-freeze response when we don't know how we feel about something. Some people call this "shutting down" and don't quite understand why it happens. Repressed emotions are when you do it unconditionally.

When repressed and suppressed emotions are left unacknowledged, unprocessed, and unexpressed, they can cause many concerns in your mental, physical, and spiritual well-being.

An example of a repressed emotion could be a person who was burnt by a birthday candle as a young child; without conscious thought of this, they later develop anxiety as an adult when seeing a flame or even smelling the scent of an extinguished candle. People with repressed emotions may frequently experience unexplained nervousness, exhibit forgetfulness, avoid conversations about their feelings, feel a sense of emotional detachment, and tend to address situations in a passive-aggressive manner.

An example of a suppressed emotion could be a person who is thought to be the "unshakable" family leader. The calm, cool, and collected person who doesn't express intense emotions often. One day, their most loved pet passes away, and they are crushed. They decide to be "tough" for the family and hide the grief. However, they begin to develop sleep issues and nightmares, headaches, and irritability by not processing the feelings and expressing the grief.

In my case, numerous traumatic experiences resulted in many repressed and suppressed emotions. Only when I confronted my fears and emotions with consistency and courage did I find the ability to let them go and move forward. Others will value and respect your authentic expressions far more than your concealed ones.

It's not all in your head

In moments of trauma, the body's stress response may lose control, leading to a dysregulation of the Autonomic Nervous System. A dysregulated or imbalanced stress response indicates an abnormal or flawed reaction to stress within the body. This implies that the body's response to stress is either too intense, inadequate, or ineffective.

There are two primary forms of dysregulated stress response

Hyperactive Stress Response:

This is an excessively reactive and easily triggered response, often resulting in an exaggerated unleashing of stress-related hormones. This can lead to chronic stress-related illnesses, weakened immune function, elevated blood pressure, heart issues, sleep disturbances, anxiety, and a variety of physical and emotional symptoms linked to heightened stress levels.

Hypoactive Stress Response:

In this weakened stress response, the release of stress hormones may be inadequate. As a result, managing stressors can become challenging. You may experience emotional numbness or be unable to cope with challenges effectively. This could contribute to a sense of disconnection and diminished motivation. Symptoms may also include chronic fatigue, muscle weakness, mood fluctuations, or prolonged pain (Bach, 2015).

Experiencing trauma, prolonged stress, early-life adversity, and specific medical conditions can all play a role in the emergence of an imbalanced stress reaction. Treatment for dysregulated stress responses often involves stress management techniques, energy healing, cognitive-behavioral therapy, Somatic Therapy, and lifestyle adjustments to help restore a more balanced system. If you've been encountering these symptoms, seeking professional evaluation and guidance is crucial. Without therapy or other forms of healing support, persistent feelings of anxiety, hypervigilance, or dissociation are likely to persist (Foa & Hearst-Ikeda, 1996). Understanding your body's systems and responses will help you develop strategies that will support your trauma healing and allow you to find relief from physical and emotional pain.

"It's far more important to know what person the disease has than what disease the person has."

-Hippocrates   (Hippocrates Quotes. n.d.)

Overview of different types of trauma Somatic Therapy could help

Physical Trauma:

This occurs when the body experiences injury or harm, such as accidents, violence, or abuse. It can result in visible wounds, pain, or impaired physical functioning.

Emotional Trauma:

Refers to psychological distress caused by events like loss, neglect, or witnessing violence. Emotional trauma may lead to intense emotions, mood swings, anxiety, depression, or difficulty in trusting others.

Sexual Trauma:

Includes sexual abuse, assault, or harassment and could cause emotional scars and spiritual pain. It can lead to feelings of shame, guilt, fear, nightmares, flashbacks, or changes in sexual behavior (Rothschild, 2000).

Relational Trauma:

Arises from harmful or abusive relationships, such as domestic violence or emotional manipulation. Its effects can include low self-esteem, difficulties in forming healthy connections, and intimacy issues.

Complex Trauma:

Occurs when someone experiences multiple or prolonged traumatic events. It can result in a range of symptoms like dissociation, self-destructive behavior, difficulties with self-regulation, and a distorted sense of self. It could also include a host of other issues depending on the traumas involved (BioBeats, 2021).

Generational Trauma:

Experts believe that generating trauma begins when a family experiences horrific events such as racism, natural disasters, war, discrimination, religious abuse, injustice, or more. The trauma of these events ripples down through generations.

Developmental Trauma:

Adverse experiences that occur during childhood, typically over a prolonged period. It can result from neglect, abuse, or other forms of chronic stress. It can disrupt emotional, cognitive, and social development, leading to long-term mental and physical wellness effects (Kolk & Bessel, 2007). Concerns may include difficulty with emotional regulation, impaired self-esteem, challenges forming healthy relationships, and disruptions in cognitive and academic functioning (Bach, 2015).

Acute Trauma:

Describes a single disturbing occurrence that surpasses your capacity to cope. This can include experiences like natural disasters, accidents, or violent incidents (Benjet et al., 2015).

Acute trauma can trigger immediate distress and a range of physical, emotional, and psychological reactions (Rothschild, 2000). Common manifestations can include intense fear, intrusive thoughts or memories, nightmares, hypervigilance, avoidance of reminders, and body changes like accelerated heart rate or perspiration. (Benjet et al., 2015)

Differences in trauma throughout the lifespan

As you know, the body is a warehouse of emotions.

Cues and markers of trauma can display differently across the lifespan, reflecting your unique experiences and developmental stages.

In children, trauma may manifest as behavioral changes, regression, difficulty concentrating, nightmares, or separation anxiety. Adolescents may display emotional instability, self-destructive behaviors, substance abuse, withdrawal from relationships, and even physical illness (Allmer et al., 2009). Adults may experience intrusive memories, emotional numbing, hypervigilance, difficulty trusting others, issues with blood pressure, stomach issues, or more.

When trauma occurs during your formative years, you need to nurture your inner child and engage in the process of re-parenting. Your inner child is the most authentic and vulnerable part of yourself formed from infancy through adolescence. It is the parts of you that are trusting, innocent, pure, and curious. Your inner child is the you before the trauma (Sapra, 2023).

Parents and caregivers are expected to safeguard your health and growth. However, at times, they may lack the resources to address their trauma, leaving the child without the tools needed to cope effectively. When trauma disrupts your inner child without healing, you will continue to experience these issues into adulthood. You can re-parent yourself by prioritizing yourself and focusing on your stability and happiness. This involves creating a nurturing and supportive connection with yourself as if you were your own loving parent of a cherished child. Re-parenting calls for cultivating self-love, self-care, boundary establishment, and potentially looking for qualified guidance. You need to address any unmet needs from your early years. Re-parenting is not about blaming your parents or caregivers. It's about taking responsibility for your healing and growth. Regardless of what age the trauma occurred, it can disrupt your sleep patterns, impair cognitive functioning, contribute to mood disorders, and impact your overall happiness. Recognizing these signs and symptoms and seeking treatment regardless of age is essential. Sometimes, as adults, we are expected to just look past things or ignore them; however, adults need help just as much as children.

Trigger-Ology 101

Triggers are scenarios, circumstances, or anything that prompts intense emotions or physical responses that you associate with a past traumatic experience (Thulin & Thulin, 2020). For me, the sound of speeding cars, emergency vehicles, or people yelling would send my body into an instant panic and flare up. Triggers activate your body's stress, just as it would to a genuine threat. It's vital to completely and precisely recognize what triggers you. This awareness is essential for acknowledging and confronting the impact of your traumatic experiences on your present behavior and emotions.

It's vital to observe repetitive patterns in your thoughts, emotions, and responses, which could be linked to unresolved trauma. If you ever find yourself overreacting to minor events, experiencing rapid anger or irritability, having flashbacks or nightmares, or facing intrusive thoughts and panic attacks, your pain points or triggers are active. You can use the awareness exercises within this book to help you figure this out (Rothschild, 2000).

Instant control over your triggers might not be possible. However, each day that you take the time to practice your somatic and other therapies, you will feel better. By learning to recognize your patterns and triggers, you will shed light on what factors shape your responses (Thulin & Thulin, 2020).

This is a required step in healing.

A few techniques for recognizing and changing your trigger patterns include naming and expressing your emotions safely, journaling, and statements. This practice helps you create new brainwave patterns for a healthier life.

To begin, take a moment to genuinely identify and share your emotional state using words, whether spoken or written. You may find the feelings chart from Chapter 3's self-reflection section helpful. Consider if you're experiencing sadness, disappointment, frustration, anger, or another emotion entirely.

Try to pinpoint this.

Journaling has been emphasized for good reason—it's an incredibly potent tool, particularly for trauma healing.

This is where you can write freely about your emotions and experiences without censoring yourself. There should be no worry of being misjudged or misunderstood. Over time, journaling aids in gaining clarity and understanding of your traumatic experience. It allows you to process emotions and address concerns without solely relying on your memory. Sometimes, with trauma, your memories can come and go; you may only remember fragments. By putting everything down in writing (or even in a voice recording device), you can help put together the pieces of your trauma and trigger puzzle.

The perfect moment to start a journal is now!

Another technique to help change your triggers is using "I" statements to express emotions when talking to others. Saying things like "I feel sad" instead of blaming or accusing them. The "I" statements require you gb to be vulnerable, which then turns down your intense triggered emotion.

The deep breathing and mindfulness exercises within this book or provided by your therapist can help connect with emotions and allow them to surface gently.

All of the exercises can help reduce your triggers over time. When you begin to understand your triggers, give yourself the space and validation needed to express them healthily and constructively. You have the ability to do this by crafting your own limits during treatment, like taking breaks when needed, using your new awareness skills to know before you are overwhelmed, and celebrating your progress, no matter how small.

The courage to seek help = the ultimate self-care

Please keep in mind these factors when looking into trauma therapy. You have to commit to getting care because it is not easy. As humans, facing ourselves and our traumas is one of the hardest things to do. There may be experiences that you think shouldn't bother you anymore or occasions that you don't want to give any more time and attention. However, the emotions most likely will persist consciously or unconsciously without care. This can permanently impair your life. It's essential to identify and express your feelings now. Make sure to practice your daily mindfulness routine to prepare for treatment (G. C. Center, 2020). During your treatment, please keep in mind that everyone is unique. The same thing that creates trauma for you may not for another. Your thoughts, reactions, and behaviors will be original to you. It is important not to compare your results to the results of others. However, support and understanding from others is incredible.

Remind yourself that you are capable of progressing without the need for approval from others to truthfully express yourself or seek treatment for your trauma. For example, some may ignore the trauma to avoid family shame. This can be a barrier to treatment; however, you must know that eventually, your family will be better when you are healed.

It's important not to deny that it happened.

You can only be healed by going through this process fully, truthfully, and authentically.

You should avoid being critical of yourself as it will make a big difference in your recovery. Try to find the middle ground of placing too much or too little pressure on yourself as you want to make progress without re-traumatization. An essential factor to keep in mind in your Somatic Therapy is the influence of your emotional connections when you've undergone trauma alongside or at the hands of someone else.

The Power of Trauma Bonding

Trauma bonding refers to a strong, often unhealthy, emotional connection formed between those who have experienced intense, distressing situations together. This bond can develop in abusive relationships, where the target feels a connection to the person causing the harm. This could be a lover, family member, companion, or even a caregiver.

In Somatic Therapy, understanding trauma bonding is vital because your therapists can address the deep emotional ties that can persist. Some people develop conflicted feelings for their abuser. It's natural to still love someone you grew up with or after investing time and energy into a relationship. You may continue to see the good in the person despite the trauma. You may still express love, compassion, and hope for the relationship, as this offers you a temporary means of managing the situation. Despite this, trauma-bonded connections can lead to long-term harm due to the continuing abuse. Understanding the biology of traumatic bonding is critical to finding ways to break free from it. Biologically speaking, the thirst for bonds originates in infancy when we rely on caregivers for survival. This foundation of attachment means that we turn to caregivers for support and comfort in times of threat, like trauma. Oxytocin, the "love hormone," reinforces this attachment, powered by low self-esteem, self-doubt, anxiety, and depression (Gimpl & Fahrenholz, 2001). In adult relationships, our significant other often becomes a caregiving figure. Trauma bonds form when our significant others, our caregivers, become the source of trauma through abusive behavior. Despite the abuse, we turn to them due to our built-in attachment instinct. Having lived with abusers, whether it be a spouse or caregiver, I understand what it's like to feel as though you have to love the devil. As the abuse is rationalized with loving actions, the bond is strengthened, making it hard to imagine life without them. Maintaining a trauma-bonded relationship can have hidden impacts like excessive cortisol production, leading to immune system issues, anxiety, and high blood pressure. To overcome trauma bonds, it's crucial not to trade truth for empty promises (Gibbons, 2019).

Recognize the enduring patterns of abuse, even in non-violent moments. Be honest about the impact of abuse on you. Acknowledge your feelings and experiences. Practice self-compassion and challenge negative self-talk with affirming truths. Build a fulfilling life without those who harm you by setting and achieving your personal goals. Before my healing journey, I was in numerous relationships marked by physical, emotional, and spiritual abuse. The most important steps I learned were how to trust myself and give myself permission to heal, get in touch with my awareness and trust my faith, and confide in someone I trusted; this gave me the strength and emotional support I needed to survive.

You may have a trauma bond if you relate to any of the following:

- Obsessing over past individuals who caused harm, despite their absence

- Seeking contact with people known to cause further pain

- Going above and beyond to aid those who have been destructive

- Remaining part of a group despite evident destructiveness

- Trying to win approval from people who exploit your kindness

- Repeatedly trusting unreliable individuals

- Struggling to distance yourself from unhealthy relationships

- Seeking understanding from those who show little care

- Choosing conflict over peace, even when walking away, is easy

- Persistently attempting to communicate a problem to unwilling listeners

- Sticking by someone who has violated your trust

- Magnetism to people with questionable reliability

- Hiding dark secrets concerning oppressive treatment or exploitation

- Reaching out to an unapologetic abuser

There are numerous actions you can take to address your trauma. Here, I've outlined my top 12 crucial steps for healing

Acknowledge and Accept the Trauma

Recognize that you've experienced something traumatic. This is a crucial first step in healing. The path to recovery is accepting your world the way it is now.

Seek Professional Help

Explore the possibility of seeking support from a qualified practitioner, particularly one well-versed in trauma.

Educate Yourself

Learn about your specific type of trauma, its effects, and coping mechanisms. For instance, a survivor of a natural disaster would experience different impacts compared to a victim of bullying.

If you struggling with Chronic or Mental illness, learn about your diagnosis. Learn why you do what you do, and you will find it easier to understand and change.

Practice Self-compassion

Treat yourself with compassion and patience. Be mindful that healing takes time, and there's no rush—taking it slow is acceptable. Trust yourself that you carry a light within that will help you.

Mindfulness and Grounding Techniques

Practices like meditation, grounding, and controlled breath exercises can keep you "in the now" and help regulate anxiety.

Journaling

Write down or voice record everything to process emotions and gain clarity. Recommend this staple for everyone.

Establish a Support System

Encircle yourself with trusted connections that can encourage you, provide insight, and relate to your perspective. Locally or online, companions, family, or support networks can provide a sense of community and calm (Heinrichs et al., 2003).

Set Limits

Learn to decline and define boundaries in order to safeguard your emotional wellness.

Physical Well-being

Place importance on your health through consistent engagement in exercise, a healthy diet, ample sleep, and self-care.

Process Grief and Loss

If the trauma involves loss, allow yourself to grieve.

Forgiveness

Consider working towards forgiving yourself and, if applicable, forgiving people that have played a role in the trauma.

Try Activities that Bring You Joy

Reconnect with things you love and find activities that typically provide you a feeling of purpose and contentment.

In the aftermath of a traumatic experience, take a moment to consider ten questions as your initial steps toward healing.

What emotions am I currently feeling about this experience?

This can help you identify and acknowledge your feelings, which is an essential step towards processing trauma.

How has this experience shaped my beliefs about myself and the world?

Traumatic experiences can significantly influence our core beliefs. Making sense of this can be a critical factor in healing.

Have I developed any coping mechanisms as a result of this experience?

People often develop various coping strategies to deal with trauma. It's vital to assess if these are healthy or if they need to be adjusted.

What prompts memories of the traumatic occurrence?

Being conscious of your triggers can assist you in planning

how to handle them better each time.

What support systems do I currently have in place?

It's important to acknowledge the people and resources available to you. This can include friends, family, therapy, support groups, etc. They will help reduce cortisol and irritability (Heinrichs et al., 2003).

Have I found any positive aspects or personal growth from this experience?

While it's natural to focus on the negative, sometimes there can be unexpected positive outcomes or personal growth from traumatic experiences.

What limits do I need to make to safeguard my well-being moving forward?

Establishing boundaries is crucial for maintaining your emotional and mental health.

What self-care rituals can I start to boost my healing?

Self-care is essential for trauma recovery. This can include physical, emotional, and mental self-care strategies.

Have I sought professional help in processing this trauma?

Seeking a qualified practitioner could supply precious insight and guidance when navigating the healing process.

What can I do to practice self-compassion and forgiveness towards myself?

Recognize the value of treating yourself with compassion and understanding. Forgiveness, both for yourself and possibly for others involved, can be a decisive step towards healing.

Trauma-specific therapies

Recovery approaches geared explicitly toward trauma often emphasize somatic or body-based therapies. These treatments zero in on guiding you toward a renewed connection with the body and finally releasing the suffering. There are therapies and techniques designed for all ages.

Cognitive Processing Therapy:

It focuses on helping you dispute and improve negative beliefs and feelings surrounding the distressing circumstance. It aims to reframe distorted thinking patterns and promote a more adaptive perspective. Helpful for PTSD, shame, and guilt (Resick et al., 2016). Generally, there are 12 weekly appointments as part of the program.

Eye Movement Desensitization and Reprocessing (EMDR):

EMDR incorporates directed eye movements or alternative methods of bilateral stimulation to assist you when revisiting distressing events. This therapy helps you work through traumatic memories and reduce their emotional intensity (G. C. Center, 2020). A more detailed description of EMDR can be found in Chapter 2.

Prolonged Exposure Therapy (PE):

The emphasis in PE is on addressing and processing memories and emotional reactions shaped by trauma within a protected and managed environment. It could help reduce avoidance mechanisms and anguish connected with traumatic memories. You will learn to recall attention to specific details, such as emotions and thoughts from within the memory. It could involve a recording made for you to listen to in between sessions to aid in emotional processing (Johnson, 2022).

You could be assigned the homework of gradually confronting feared situations tied to the trauma. This would be done independently outside of the session. Take good notes about your experiences. It may aid with PTSD. Average number of sessions is 8-15. Seek a certified PE trainer.

Trauma-Focused Cognitive-Behavioral Therapy (TF-CBT):

TF-CBT is tailor-made for the unique requirements of kids and teens living with trauma. This approach blends thought and response-related practices, trauma processing, and skill-building exercises (Dorsey et al., 2016). For ages 3-18, typical sessions last up to 1 hour. Look for a mental health practitioner certified in TF-CBT (National Children's Advocacy Center, n.d.).

Narrative Exposure Therapy (NET):

In NET, you will generate an detailed account of the distressing occurrences to help you gain perspective and process the events in a structured manner. You may review your entire life, not just the bad memories, to help you put things into perspective. May aid with PTSD and Complex Trauma. Often used for survivors of war and refugees. Typically has 8-12 sessions that last 1 to 1 ½ hours. Look for a NET-trained practitioner (H. Center, 2023).

Somatic Experiencing® (SE™):

Focuses on helping you release physical tension and energy associated with trauma through body awareness and movement. Explored with further specifics in Chapters 2 and 6.

Sensorimotor Psychotherapy:

This therapy incorporates mindfulness and body-centered techniques to help you cope with and let go of traumatic memories held in the body (Ogden et al., 2006). Described with more detail in Chapter 2.

Group Therapy:

Group therapy geared towards trauma aims to allow you to share your experiences, gain support, and learn coping skills in a safe and empathetic environment. You can search online or ask your therapist for recommendations to find a group related to your trauma experience.

Seeking Safety®:

This therapy is designed by Lisa M Najavits to address trauma and substance abuse, providing skills to manage both issues at once. This treatment does not require you to share detailed explanations of your trauma. It focuses on building coping skills and emotional regulation. Depending on your therapist's assessment, attending 12-25 sessions is typical (Najavits, 2015). Explore options for a emotional wellness expert who has completed the Seeking Safety® course (Seeking Safety, n.d.). In the next chapter, we'll explore how to set goals for your therapy, the role of the therapist, how to find treatment and other complementary practices. We'll look at how somatic and traditional therapy comes together.

Chapter 8: Starting Your Healing Journey: Time to Unleash Your Body's Superpowers!

What to expect in this chapter:

Preparing to start Somatic Therapy
Defining your personal goals and intentions
Establish a network of therapeutic support
Expectations & roles for you and your therapist
How to find a somatic therapist or practitioner
Traditional Medicine & Energy healing

"No tree becomes rooted and sturdy unless many a wind assails it. For by its very tossing it tightens its grip and plants its roots more securely; the fragile trees are those that have grown in a sunny valley."
— Seneca   (Seneca the Younger. n.d.)

Preparing to start Somatic Therapy

Laying the foundation for your Somatic Therapy experience

Preparing to start Somatic Therapy calls for you to be mentally and emotionally ready for a shifting reality. You can never guess how you will feel or know what will be discovered. For optimal results, it is essential to invest in cultivating emotional flexibility and a proactive mindset to navigate the challenges that you will face. How could you manifest this in your life? It's about being in step with your current emotional and physical needs. I compel you to embrace all healing opportunities with confidence and clarity. Being ready means being open to new experiences and adaptable to change. It's about welcoming self-reflection, learning, and infusing life with meaning and intention. If you go into therapy doubting yourself or not trusting the process, you simply cannot create the peace you are looking for.

You must fully and honestly look at your willingness to explore the physical aspect of feelings and past experiences. Initially, the therapist may evaluate whether you possess a foundational level of emotional stability and the ability to manage potentially intense or unfamiliar bodily sensations. They will also consider your motivation and commitment to engage in somatic work. Being honest and open to yourself and your therapist about your true feelings is vital.

It's not the right place to be reserved.or ignore what is happening.

I get that, occasionally, you may be comfortable overlooking certain things. You may believe acknowledging what's bothering you would grant it more significance. I certainly didn't want to invest any more time discussing something I'd already devoted years of misery to. I didn't want to give the monster any more power over me. However, it wasn't until I "walked through the fire" of full acknowledgment and awareness that I was brought closer to peace.

To streamline the process, come prepared to talk about your expectations, concerns, and goals for therapy before your consultation. These steps will guarantee that you are well-prepared for the best possible results.

How to define your goals beforehand

Defining your personal goals and intentions for therapy involves a process of introspection and purposeful focus. Within the framework of what led you to seek treatment, you will pinpoint distinct goals, desires, and areas requiring improvement.

This can include anything related to your physical or emotional healing, self-discovery, or personal transformation, whatever is most pressing to you.

Personal goals will serve as beacons that will guide your therapeutic process. By clarifying these goals now, you will set a clear trajectory for your healing (Lawlor & Hornyak, 2012). This will give you a spark of inspiration right at the start. An example set of goals could be to get to the root cause of your low self-esteem, build positive self-worth, create better-coping mechanisms when stressed, and reduce your triggers (Kropf, 2023).

These goals will provide a more focused exploration of your concerns and result in a more personalized treatment plan. They will allow for measurable progress in your therapy. Setting goals and intentions equips you to play an active role in healing, creating a collaborative partnership between you and your therapist. Following these steps, you can define meaningful personal goals and create intentions to guide your Somatic Therapy experience.

Here's a detailed blueprint to help you:

Reflection:

Carve out a moment to think about your life right now including challenges and expectations. List all areas of your life that you wish to improve or explore through Somatic Therapy. A sample list might include improving stress management, healing from trauma, deepening body awareness, better communication, balanced relationships, strengthening mind-body connection, and setting healthy boundaries through Somatic Therapy.

Identify Priorities:

Prioritize the list in the order that resonates with you the most. Think about which aspects of your relationships or personal growth you want to focus on first.

Be Specific:

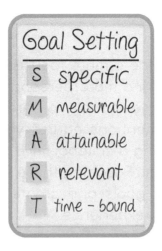

Define the objectives with clarity, ensuring they are specific, measurable, attainable, relevant, and time-bound or SMART (Kropf, 2023). This ensures transparency and the ability to gauge the progress of your goals.

An example is:

Specific: I'll express more gratitude in my daily journal

Measurable: I'll write things I'm grateful for every night

Attainable: I will do this for five minutes before bed

Relevant: I want to be happier and more thankful in my life

Time-bound: I'll do this every night for three months starting tomorrow

Smart Goal creation worksheets and tracker are available in the companion book, "The Blessing: Workbook and Journal of Life with Gratitude" by Naty H.E.A.L.S.

Explore Intentions:

Dive deeper into any underlying intentions behind your goals. Think about why the goals are important and how achieving them will align with your values and expectations.

For example, I value this goal because managing my intense emotions is important for my emotional well-being and for gaining peace within my household. This will bring balance and love to my life. Achieving this goal will help me to handle challenges with greater care and respect.

Body Awareness:

As you set your goals, try using somatic practices like body scans or mindful movement to connect with your bodily sensations. Notice how your body responds to each goal and intention when you think, write, or say it aloud. Observe any changes in your sensations. Perhaps there's a release of tension or a feeling of warmth. Is there a lightness, a sense of openness, or maybe a tingling sensation?

Commitment:

Commit yourself and your goals. Write them down, create visual reminders, or share them with a supportive person to motivate and solidify your dedication. Remember, all healing starts with you.

Action Plan:

Create a detailed plan linked to your goals, outlining the necessary steps, resources, and backing required to reach the goal, such as obtaining a journal or securing an appointment with a practitioner.

Review and Adjust:

Over time, regularly review your goals and expectations, assess your progress, and go on to the next goal.

Establish a network of therapeutic support

Building a therapeutic support network requires creating a web of relationships and resources to assist you along your therapy journey. Connecting with others who offer empathetic understanding, guidance, and validation is essential. These connections can be formed through friendships, family bonds, support groups, group therapy, or online communities. If you are comfortable, choose at least one person to share what you have been experiencing, someone who can empathize with you.

The road to healing is rough, with many potholes along the way. A therapeutic support network serves as your safety net during challenging times (Holt-Lunstad et al., 2010). They can provide comfort, encouragement, and a private space to share your vulnerabilities. This will help the road feel less bumpy. It's priceless to open up to someone about your thoughts and receive upliftment and empathic encouragement. Initiating contact with others and maintaining these relationships will provide you a sense of belonging (Heinrichs et al., 2003). The knowledge that you are not alone is such a powerful emotional resource.

Expectations for you and your therapist

Your therapist's responsibility is to offer a secure and nurturing space, setting the stage for healing and growth. During your therapy, you should feel secure, respected, and understood. They are trained to achieve this through clear communication, empathy, and active listening. The physical environment should be welcoming, comfortable, and free from distractions. Preserving trust and privacy are key, enabling you to express your worries unburdened by the fear of criticism. The therapist's presence should be nurturing, compassionate, and attuned to your needs. It's important to understand that contacting several practitioners may be necessary to locate your ideal match. Even if you start with a therapist and later discover that it is not a match, do not be afraid to explore other options. You will need to set realistic expectations for your treatment. This will require you to research and understand the specific nature of your chosen therapy, including the potential outcomes and complications.

It's essential to recognize that healing with Somatic Therapy is a approach that takes time and work. It took years from hitting my lowest point to start taking meaningful steps toward changing my life. Realistic expectations involve acknowledging that progress might happen gradually. It may not provide instant or divine results, but you will feel better. Somatic Therapy can bring about positive changes in your physical and emotional wellness; however, it may not entirely remove all of your challenges or difficulties alone. By setting practical expectations, you can approach your treatment with patience, commitment, and a willingness to engage in this transformative process. At times, you might need to push past your comfort zone and challenge yourself and your beliefs and ideas. When starting a journey with Somatic Therapy, self-compassion and patience become essential. Grant yourself the gift of gentleness and acceptance. Being patient will allow space for your emotional and spiritual growth. It will also make it simpler to embrace any setbacks you may have. Remember that even the slightest change is a step on the right path. For the relationship to be most effective, you and the therapist must dedicate your complete and undivided attention to each other.

The role of therapists and practitioners

The role of a somatic therapist is to open the door to healing and growth by working with the synergy between the body and mind. Therapists are trained professionals who have expertise and understanding in addressing the somatic, emotional, and psychological aspects of you.

Another role of a somatic therapist is to help you find harmony or coherence. Coherence combines how you feel in your body, what you think, and how you behave. When you have coherence, it's like your body and feelings are in sync. You feel balanced and at ease.

Breakdown of what to expect:

Assessment and Diagnosis:

Somatic therapists assess and diagnose your physical and emotional issues. They take into account your unique experiences, symptoms, and goals. They gather information about your history, current challenges, and any trauma or significant life events that may impact your wellness.

Mind-Body Integration:

Somatic therapists recognize and emphasize the interwoven relationship of the mind and body. They will help deepen your understanding of the connection between your physical and emotional reactions. Through various techniques, they will guide you to integrate multiple physical and psychological experiences to promote your healing and growth.

Developing Somatic Awareness:

Somatic therapists assist you in developing greater awareness of your movements and postures. They help you identify and understand the somatic markers left by your emotions and stress responses.

How to find a somatic therapist or practitioner

Research:

Start by researching more about the exact Somatic Therapy you are interested in, exploring locally or online. Have a good understanding of its principles, approaches, and benefits before your first appointment.

Referrals and Recommendations:

Seek referrals and recommendations from trusted sources, such as loved ones, close companions, or healthcare professionals who may have experience with Somatic Therapy.

Don't know anyone personally? It's ok. Investigate online for user reviews for a potential therapist.

Online Directories:

Utilize online directories designed explicitly for finding therapists. Websites like Psychology Today®, GoodTherapy®, and TherapyDen® often include search filters allowing you to narrow your search to somatic therapists in your area.

There is also a compiled list of online directories available on my website.

Professional Associations:

Check professional associations and organizations related to your Somatic Therapy of choice. These groups typically have databases or recommendations to assist you in locating a certified professional. For example, the Somatic Experiencing® Trauma Institute or SETI has a directory of SE™ practitioners.

Local Mental Health Centers or Clinics:

Inquire if they have somatic therapists on staff or if they can provide recommendations for resources in your community.

After you have found a few therapists that feel like a good match. It's time to verify their credentials and book your initial consultation(s).

Verify Credentials and Licensure:

First, make sure the therapist is appropriately licensed or has the required qualifications and certifications. Verify their credentials through a professional licensing board or the organization that issued the certificate.

Initial Consultations:

Compile a list of at least two therapists you're interested in (if financially possible) and arrange an initial consultation with both. This is your chance to articulate your needs and get a sense of their approach and expertise. Finding a therapist who gives you a sense of ease and confidence is key.

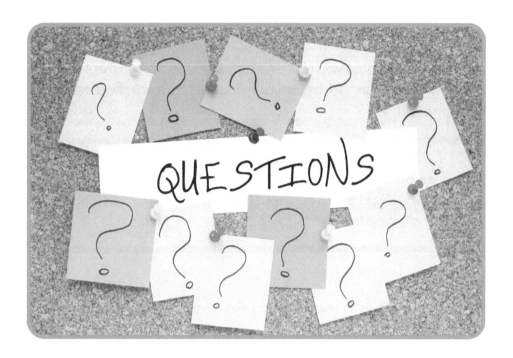

Here are a few sample points to discuss during the consultation.

What is your experience and training in Somatic Therapy?

Understanding the therapist's background and qualifications is vital to see if they have the necessary training and experience.

Can you explain your approach to Somatic Therapy?

This question allows the therapist to explain their theoretical orientation and how they blend somatic methods into the therapeutic approach.

How can Somatic Therapy help with my specific concerns?

This question helps you understand the therapist's perspective on how they can address your individualized requirements and difficulties.

What types of techniques do you typically use?

Understanding a specific therapist's techniques can help you gauge their approach.

How do you adjust your strategy to my unique needs?

Exploring this will shed light into the therapist's ability to customize their approach based on your specific situation and preferences.

How many sessions can I expect and what is the duration of the sessions?

Understanding the logistics of the therapy process can help you plan your commitment and integrate it into your life

How do you integrate talk therapy and somatic work in your sessions?

Some therapists may combine traditional talk therapy with somatic techniques. It's helpful to know how they balance these approaches.

What are your goals for our therapeutic work together?

This question will offer a perspective of what the therapist hopes to achieve and whether their goals align with yours.

How do you maintain a secure and comfortable setting during sessions? Do you offer services online?

Feeling safe is crucial in therapy. This question helps you understand the therapist's approach to creating a safe space for somatic work.

How do you handle any potential emotional or physical discomfort during sessions?

Somatic Therapy can sometimes bring up strong emotions or physical sensations. Understanding how the therapist handles these situations is critical.

Do you assign homework or practice between sessions?

Some therapists may provide exercises or practices to work on between sessions. This question can help you prepare for the therapeutic process.

How will you measure my progress in therapy?

It's helpful to know how the therapist tracks your progress and evaluates the effectiveness of the therapy.

Remember that the initial consultation is a two-way process. It's not just about the therapist evaluating if they can help you but also about you gauging if the practitioner aligns with your vibe and comfort level. Don't hesitate to ask any additional questions that are important to you.

Are you already in talk therapy or other therapies? Perfect!

The integration of Somatic Therapy with talk therapy creates a powerful synergy. The combination will give access to a deeper level of healing. As traditional therapy focuses on cognitive processes, Somatic Therapy adds your body to the picture, supercharging the therapeutic process. By integrating these modalities, you can gain an even more holistic understanding of yourself. The bridge to whole body health

Traditional medicine and energy healing can supercharge your Somatic Therapy. Traditional medicine refers to ancient health practices, approaches, and knowledge. It often incorporates plant, wildlife, and mineral-rich remedies, soul-centered practices, hands-on methods, and sessions to not only treat, diagnose, and prevent illnesses but also maintain your health. They have consistently recognized the profound synergy in the realm of mind-body connection. By understanding and utilizing the mind-body connection, traditional medicine has long been the standard for supreme health. Traditional medicines have been proven to treat both chronic illness as well as mental health concerns. They aim to restore balance, regulate your emotions, and alleviate stress and anxiety. For millennia, people worldwide have practiced traditional medicine. Diverse forms exist globally, originating from regions like China, Africa, India, Europe, Iran, and Korea. Somatic Therapy can be enhanced by the incorporation of traditional medicine practices (The Persistence of Traditional Medicine in the Modern World, 2023).

Here's a list of traditional medicine approaches you might consider exploring.

Traditional Chinese Medicine (TCM):

TCM involves an assortment of methods like, acupuncture, Plant-based treatments, nutrition, massage (Tui Na), and exercises like Tai Chi and Qi Gong. It aims to harmonize the body's energy, renew equilibrium, and promote total health.

Acupuncture:

This commonly used TCM practice utilizes the placement of fine needles into precise places on the body to activate and stabilize the flow of energy called Qi, also known as Chi. Can help with neck pain and quailty of life (MacPherson et al., 2015).

Ayurveda:

My main area of study is Ayurveda, an ancient traditional medical system dating back over 5000 years. It stands among the oldest known systems of medicine. Although it is more than just medicine, it is a way of life. This time-tested Indian whole-body healing approach centers on cultivating peace and unity in the trinity of body, mentality, and soul. It utilizes personalized approaches, including herbal medicine, diet, lifestyle modifications, and yoga. The practice also incorporates spiritual knowledge, memory, meditation, and patience (Adil, 2023).

A daily Ayurvedic routine is customized to everyone; however, some principles are recommended daily. For example, a typical day could include transcendental meditation, oil pulling, yoga, and a light walk in the morning. Then, have your main meal midday, followed by evening transcendental meditation. One of the main principles of Ayurveda is regarding a healthy diet and digestion(Adil, 2023).

> "When diet is wrong, medicine is of no use; When diet is correct, medicine is of no need."
> (Ayurvedic Proverb)   (Exclamation & Exclamation, 2021)

This quote guides us to take care and eat a proper diet personalized to our distinct body type. When you go in sync with the laws of nature, you create a barrier against diseases. Sleep is also an essential practice in Ayurveda. Sleep can bring happiness and nourishment, allowing your body to balance and recover from the day (Exclamation & Exclamation, 2021).

Traditional Korean Medicine (TKM):

TKM integrates acupuncture, herbal medicine, cupping therapy, and other techniques to address imbalances and promote health Lee et al. (2018). Cupping therapy involves placing glass suction cups on painful parts of your body, creating a vacuum to restore Qi's flow (Kang et al., 2017).

Kampo Medicine:

Kampo is a traditional Japanese herbal medicine system from ancient Chinese medicine. It utilizes herbal formulas to restore balance and address various health conditions, including gastrointestinal tract disorders and depression, to name a few (Ishida & Sato, 2006).

Traditional Native American medicine:

These healing practices have been passed down from generation to generation within indigenous societies throughout North America. Many distinct regions and cultures fall into this category. There is a focus on the harmonious link between mind, body, and nature. This approach could include elements such as herbal remedies, rituals, energy practices, and storytelling (Le, 1999). It could be used for energy imbalances, seeking spiritual insight, or addressing multiple physical, mental, emotional, and spiritual concerns (Cohen, 1998.)

Siddha Medicine:

Siddha medicine is a traditional South Indian healing system that emphasizes using herbs, minerals, and other natural substances to restore health. It is similar to Ayurveda, with distinct differences in philosophy and diagnosis techniques. It incorporates practices like yoga and meditation. It treats everything from allergies, migraines, stomach issues, skin diseases, and more (SIDDHA SOLUTION FOR CHRONIC DISEASES, n.d.).

Unani Medicine:

Originating from ancient Greece, this holistic healing system is widely practiced in the Middle East, South Asia, and other regions. It utilizes herbal remedies, dietary recommendations, and physical therapies to reestablish harmony and vitality. In Unani medicine, eight diagnostic methods are employed: pulse, stool, urine, tongue, speech, vision, touch, and appearance. Treatments could include massage, baths, sauna, exercise, bloodletting, cupping, and leech therapy (The Editors of Encyclopaedia Britannica, 2023).

Curanderismo:

The genesis of this traditional healing method can be traced to Latin American and Latino traditions, with a strong influence from Mexico and Central America. The practice could prove effective for pain relief, emotional healing, spiritual development, energy balancing, and addressing concerns like headaches and digestive issues (Hoogasian &

Lijtmaer, 2010). It incorporates herbal remedies, baths, energy practices, spiritual cleansing, massage, and even bone setting (Applewhite, 1995).

As the descriptions show, many traditional medicines center around concepts like Qi or life force energy.

Now, let's learn more about harnessing your body's energy system for healing

Energy healing

These practices focus on bringing back harmony and encouraging healing using your body's Qi or energy system. It recognizes that energetic imbalances or blockages can create physical, emotional, or spiritual disturbances. Qi, aka Chi, is described in Chapter 6 in the yoga section.

Energy healers apply a variety of methods to activate the movement of Qi, remove internal blockages in your meridian pathways, and support your body's natural healing abilities. The underlying principle is that you will reduce stress and anxiety by addressing energetic disturbances. Combined with Somatic Therapy, which focuses on the body, it can alleviate physical and emotional discomfort.

Here are some potential ailments related to blocked or imbalanced Qi

- Stress

- Anxiety

- Fatigue

- Menstrual Irregularities

- Headaches

- Pain and stiffness

- Indigestion

- Constipation

- Poor circulation

- Mood swings

- Fibromyalgia

- And many more

Energy healing practices that can complement your Somatic Therapy

Reiki:

Another fundamental aspect of my practice is Reiki. This can involve gently laying hands, hands hovering over your body, or even just the energy from a voice. This energy practice can help remove blockages and revitalize the organic circulation of life energy to promote healing. This can promote deep relaxation and activate your body's natural healing abilities. This process heals you from the inside out by touching every cell throughout your body. Life energy flows through all living things, and a Reiki Master can channel and direct this energy.

Pranic Healing:

Prana is the Sanskrit term for Qi. It manipulates and balances prana to cleanse and energize the body. It involves removing energetic blockages and restoring harmony. As part of the process, you may learn to absorb prana from the air and channel it into your body.

Crystal Healing:

Crystal healing harnesses the energetic qualities of crystals and gemstones to harmonize, purify, and align the body's energy. These crystals are positioned on or near your body to ease healing. Your body contains hubs for energy known as chakras, with seven primary ones running along your spine. Every one of the chakras is linked to various somatic, spiritual, and emotional characteristics such as organs, self-esteem, and connectedness (Tnn, 2019).

Quantum Healing:

Quantum healing incorporates concepts from quantum physics. It focuses on the energetic connection between the mind, body, and spirit. It recognizes that your thoughts can influence the flow of information between your cells and organs, so good thoughts and attitudes are good for the body. (Sinha, 2023) A typical session could utilize hypnosis and visualization to promote healing.

Qi Gong:

The Chinese art of Qi Gong involves the integration of motion, controlled breathing, and meditation to nourish and harmonize the life energy. It involves taking in slow, long, and deep breaths. Movements are gentle and smooth, with a focus on emotional regulation. It could help those with Fibromyalgia, Parkinson's disease, high blood pressure and COPD (Qigong: What You Need to Know, n.d.).

Energy healing techniques, often involving light or no touch, can potentially alleviate stress and anxiety, improve sleep, and alleviate pain (Qigong: What You Need to Know, n.d.). If any of these traditional medicine or energy healing practices capture your curiosity and you'd like to give it a go, follow the same steps laid out for seeking a somatic therapist. I highly recommend adding at least one of these into your new wellness regimen.

PAIN IS REAL
BUT SO IS
HOPE

Epilogue

Y ou now have everything you need to start on your path to healing. Free the stagnant energy in your body and mind and watch it thrive. It's up to you to consciously and purposefully build this connection. This is the key to meaningful healing.

The blessing is yours; you just have to take it.

Trust in the process.

Believe in your natural strength.

Embrace a life of true vitality and wellness.

It's your job to change your perspective.

Growing up in a conservative religion, I know how hard changing perspectives can be.

Embrace change, as it's inevitable for growth.

Shift your misery to love.

Throw all of the garbage out.

Time is the most valuable resource you have. Spend it wisely.

As you begin to feel better, keep being grateful for making strides, no matter how small. Sometimes, these steps ahead look like steps back at first; this is part of the process.

Remember, you are truly limitless.

Being open to love also means being open to pain as life comes and goes. Your life is worthwhile; don't waste it being miserable.

Keep diving deeper into your learning and healing practice as you will begin to attract the things you only dreamed of. This is a lifelong learning pilgrimage. Look toward the abundant possibilities that lie ahead. True inner peace.

Infuse everything you learned into the core of your daily habits.

What can your life look like in the next month, in one year, or five years if you start now?

If you are feeling in a way you don't like, you must go get it. If you feel lost or lonely, you must seek out opportunities to make the connections you need. If you are feeling "stuck" on one emotion like anger or sadness, it is your job to make time for self-care. It's all up to you to talk to others and do your self-care.

Trust in your innate capacity for emotional abundance and overflowing positivity. Who you are after trauma and stress doesn't have to be who you are forever. One pivotal lesson I've learned is to not put off until tomorrow what I can do today until tomorrow. Today is your day!

Parents, make sure to give yourself appreciation too! While you might often let your children know how proud you are of them, it's equally important to acknowledge your own efforts and be proud of yourself. Embrace every achievement with gratitude and humility. With every milestone, your determination vividly displays your faith and personal growth. Take a second to think about how far you have already progressed and where you wanna go. You don't need anyone else to acknowledge it to feel good. Your healing journey starts with your decision to transform your own life. Taking that first step is not just important; it's empowering. Your story, your strength, your healing – all in your hands. I'm here to help.

I invite you to discover additional resources and guidance on my website, www.natyheals.com. You can learn more about my journey and services or find other resources for natural healing. I've dedicated myself to a life of service, so if you need help, I will help you the best way I can. By experiencing the gentle energy healing of Reiki, you can alleviate stress, promote relaxation, and enhance your body's natural ability to heal.

To check out my website; natyheals.com

scan this QR code

I would appreciate your honest review on Amazon for this book.

Scan the code below to share your feedback. You can also discover my other projects. Thank you!

Location of one of my many blessings

Here is a poem I wrote after my healing process began:

I know you God

I know you in the joy I find in life

I know you in the Love I feel for others

I know you in the Love that I received

To see you is to appreciate the beauty of Creation

To see you is to appreciate this everlasting Love

A Love so great it is found in our inner most desires

I once believed I had to search to find you

I once believed I was not worthy of your Love

I once believed you wanted no part of me

I finally found the gift you left me

I finally found the truth you left encoded in my heart

That to find the truth I must

First seek within me

-Naty

I Know you God!

I know you in the joy I find in life
I know you in the Love I feel for others
I know you in the Love that I received
    To see you is to appreciate the beauty of Creation.
    To see you is to appreciate this everlasting Love.
    A Love so great it is found in our inner most
        ~ Desires ~

I once believed I had to search to find you.
I once believed I was not worthy of your Love
I once believed You wanted no part of me.

    I finally found the gift you left me

    I finally found the truth you left
            encoded in my heart
    That to find the truth I must
        first seek within Me

                        ~ Natalia

References

A new theory of consciousness: the mind exists as a field connected to the brain - SAND. (n.d.). A New Theory of Consciousness: The Mind Exists as a Field Connected to the Brain - SAND. https://www.scienceandnonduality.com/article/a-new-theory-of-consciousness-the-mind-exists-as-a-field-connected-to-the-brain

A quote by Lao Tzu. (n.d.). https://www.goodreads.com/quotes/4111292-if-you-are-depressed-you-are-living-in-the-past

Adil. (2023). Psychosomatic Diseases In Ayurveda. *EliteAyurveda Blog & Articles.* https://eliteayurveda.com/blog/psychosomatic-diseases-in-ayurveda/

Admin, & Admin. (2023). Art Therapy: Process, Benefits, Effectiveness. *The Human Condition.* https://thehumancondition.com/art-therapy/

Admin_Feldenkrais. (n.d.). *About the Feldenkrais Method.* Feldenkrais Method. https://feldenkrais.com/about-the-feldenkrais-method/#

Akashi, Y., Goldstein, D. S., Barbaro, G., & Umemura, T. (2008). Takotsubo cardiomyopathy. *Circulation, 118*(25), 2754–2762. https://doi.org/10.1161/circulationaha.108.767012

Allmer, C., Ventegodt, S., Kandel, I., & Merrick, J. (2009). REVIEW

ARTICLES. *International Journal of Adolescent Medicine and Health*. https://doi.org/10.1515/ijamh.2009.21.3.281

Anatomography. (2015, October 30). *HPA-axis - anterior view (with text).svg*. Wikimedia Commons. https://upload.wikimedia.org/wikipedia/commons/c/c5/HPA-axis_-_anterior_view_%28with_text%29.svg

Andersson, G., Cuijpers, P., Carlbring, P., Riper, H., & Hedman, E. (2014). Guided Internet-based vs. face-to-face cognitive behavior therapy for psychiatric and somatic disorders: a systematic review and meta-analysis. *World Psychiatry, 13*(3), 288–295. https://doi.org/10.1002/wps.20151

Applewhite, S. L. (1995). Curanderismo: Demystifying the health beliefs and practices of elderly Mexican Americans. *Health & Social Work, 20*(4), 247–253. https://doi.org/10.1093/hsw/20.4.247

Aristotle Quotes. (n.d.). BrainyQuote.com. Retrieved December 11, 2023, from BrainyQuote.com Web site: https://www.brainyquote.com/quotes/aristotle_132211

Aristotle Quotes. (n.d.). BrainyQuote.com. Retrieved December 10, 2023, from BrainyQuote.com Web site: https://www.brainyquote.com/quotes/aristotle_117887

'Arnold, L. M., Clauw, D. J., & McCarberg, B. (2011). Improving the recognition and diagnosis of fibromyalgia. *Mayo Clinic Proceedings, 86*(5), 457–464. https://doi.org/10.4065/mcp.2010.0738

Bell, E., Willson, M. C., Wilman, A. H., Dave, S., & Silverstone, P. H. (2006). Males and females differ in brain activation during cognitive tasks. *NeuroImage*, *30*(2), 529–538. https://doi.org/10.1016/j.neuroimage.2005.09.049

Benjamin Franklin Quotes. (n.d.). BrainyQuote.com. Retrieved December 10, 2023, from BrainyQuote.com Web site: https://www.brainyquote.com/quotes/benjamin_franklin_151664

Benjet, C., Bromet, E. J., Karam, E. G., Kessler, R. C., McLaughlin, K. A., Ruscio, A. M., Shahly, V., Stein, D. J., Petukhova, M., Hill, E., Alonso, J., Atwoli, L., Bunting, B., Bruffaerts, R., Caldas-De-Almeida, J. M., De Girolamo, G., Florescu, S., Gureje, O., Huang, Y., . . . Koenen, K. C. (2015). The epidemiology of traumatic event exposure worldwide: results from the World Mental Health Survey Consortium. *Psychological Medicine*, *46*(2), 327–343. https://doi.org/10.1017/s0033291715001981

BioBeats. (2021, December 13). How unprocessed trauma is stored in the body - BioBeats - Medium. *Medium*. https://medium.com/@biobeats/how-unprocessed-trauma-is-stored-in-the-body-10222a76cbad#:~:text=Like%20a%20virus%20in%20our,imprint%20of%20past%20traumatic%20events.

Bioenergetic Analysis (BA) - European Association for Psychotherapy. (2019, June 6). European Association for Psychotherapy. https://www.europsyche.org/approaches/bioenergetic-analysis/

Bloch-Atefi, A., & Ja, S. (2015). The Effectiveness of Body-Oriented

Ashton, M. (2022). The history of breathwork. *Alchemy of Breath: Breathwork Training and Events.* https://alchemyofbreath. com/the-history-of-breathwork/#:~:text=Leonard%20Orr%20 discovered%20and%20developed,with%20various%20 deep%20breathing%20patterns.

Aston-Jones, G., Rajkowski, J., & Cohen, J. D. (2000). Locus coeruleus and regulation of behavioral flexibility and attention. In *Elsevier eBooks* (pp. 165–182). https://doi.org/10.1016/s0079-6123(00)26013-5

Bach, D. (2015, April 20). *Study shows early environment has a lasting impact on stress response systems.* UW News. https:// www.washington.edu/news/2015/04/20/study-shows-early-environment-has-a-lasting-impact-on-stress-response-systems/#:~:text=A%20dulled%20stress%20response%20 system,as%20aggression%20and%20behavioral%20problems.

Baron-Cohen, S. (2004). The Essential Difference: The Truth about the Male and Female Brain. *The Journal of Men's Health & Gender,* 1(1), 98. https://doi.org/10.1016/j.jmhg.2004.03.024

Barratt, B. (2013). *The Emergence of Somatic Psychology and Bodymind Therapy.* Palgrave Macmillan.

Beauchaine, T. P. (2001). Vagal tone, development, and Gray's motivational theory: Toward an integrated model of autonomic nervous system functioning in psychopathology. *Development and Psychopathology,* 13(2), 183–214. https://doi.org/10.1017/ s0954579401002012

Psychotherapy: A Review of the Literature. *Psychotherapy and Counselling Journal of Australia*, *3*(1). https://doi.org/10.59158/001c.71153

Block, N., & Dennett, D. C. (1993). Consciousness explained. *The Journal of Philosophy*, *90*(4), 181. https://doi.org/10.2307/2940970

Boidy, J., RN. (2023). How to Prepare Yourself for EMDR Therapy: 12 Steps (with Pictures). *wikiHow*. https://www.wikihow.com/Prepare-Yourself-for-EMDR-Therapy#:~:text=Before%20the%20actual%20EMDR%20therapy,traumatic%20memories%20discussed%20during%20therapy.

Bracha, H. S. (2004). Freeze, Flight, Fight, Fright, Faint: Adaptationist perspectives on the acute stress response spectrum. *CNS Spectrums*, *9*(9), 679–685. https://doi.org/10.1017/s1092852900001954

Brandl, A., Bartsch, K., James, H., Miller, M. E., & Schleip, R. (2022). Influence of Rolfing Structural Integration on active range of Motion: A Retrospective cohort study. *Journal of Clinical Medicine*, *11*(19), 5878. https://doi.org/10.3390/jcm11195878

Brassard, P., Pelletier, C., Martin, M., Gagné, N., Poirier, P., Ainslie, P. N., Caouette, M., & Bussières, J. S. (2014). Influence of Norepinephrine and Phenylephrine on Frontal Lobe Oxygenation During Cardiopulmonary Bypass in Patients with Diabetes. Journal of Cardiothoracic and Vascular Anesthesia, 28(3), 608–617. https://doi.org/10.1053/j.jvca.2013.09.006

Brom, D., Stokar, Y. N., Lawi, C., Nuriel-Porat, V., Ziv, Y., Lerner, K., &

Ross, G. (2017). Somatic Experiencing for Posttraumatic Stress Disorder: A Randomized Controlled Outcome study. *Journal of Traumatic Stress*, *30*(3), 304–312. https://doi.org/10.1002/jts.22189

Buddha Quotes. (n.d.). BrainyQuote.com. Retrieved December 11, 2023, from BrainyQuote.com Web site: https://www.brainyquote.com/quotes/buddha_385920

Buddha Quotes. (n.d.). BrainyQuote.com. Retrieved December 11, 2023, from BrainyQuote.com Web site: https://www.brainyquote.com/quotes/buddha_121308

Buddha Quotes. (n.d.). BrainyQuote.com. Retrieved December 9, 2023, from BrainyQuote.com Web site: https://www.brainyquote.com/quotes/buddha_141546

Buddha Quotes. (n.d.). BrainyQuote.com. Retrieved December 10, 2023, from BrainyQuote.com Web site: https://www.brainyquote.com/quotes/buddha_101052

Budzynski, T. (1978). Biofeedback applications to stress-related disorders. Applied Psychology, 27(2), 73–79. https://doi.org/10.1111/j.1464-0597.1978.tb00360.x

Cannon, W. B. (1915). *Bodily changes in pain, hunger, fear and rage: An account of recent researches into the function of emotional excitement.* https://doi.org/10.1037/10013-000

Caspari, M., & Massa, H. (2012). Rolfing structural integration. In *Elsevier eBooks* (pp. 303–309). https://doi.org/10.1016/b978-0-7020-3425-1.00003-9

Center, G. C. (2020). How to Prepare for EMDR Therapy. *Greenwood Counseling Center*. https://greenwoodcounselingcenter.com/how-to-prepare-for-emdr-therapy/

Center, H. (2023, April 6). *What is Narrative Exposure Therapy?* Hanley Center. https://www.hanleycenter.org/what-is-narrative-exposure-therapy/#:~:text=If%20you%20are%20considering%20seeking,sensory%20information%2C%20and%20physiological%20responses.

Charles Dickens Quotes. (n.d.). BrainyQuote.com. Retrieved December 10, 2023, from BrainyQuote.com Web site: https://www.brainyquote.com/quotes/charles_dickens_121978

Chavan, P. (2017, May 12). What drinking cold water does to your body will shock you! | TheHealthSite.com. *TheHealthSite*. https://www.thehealthsite.com/diseases-conditions/cold-water-po0315-275162/#:~:text=Studies%20have%20shown%20that%20drinking,involuntary%20actions%20of%20the%20body.

Chief Seattle Quotes. (n.d.). BrainyQuote.com. Retrieved December 12, 2023, from BrainyQuote.com Web site: https://www.brainyquote.com/quotes/chief_seattle_140705

Choosing Therapy. (2022). Sensorimotor Psychotherapy: How It Works, Cost, & What to Expect. *Choosing Therapy*. https://www.choosingtherapy.com/sensorimotor-psychotherapy/

Choosing Therapy. (2023). Breathwork: How It Works, Effectiveness, & Tips for Getting Started. *Choosing*

Therapy. https://www.choosingtherapy.com/breathwork/

Chevalier, G., Sinatra, S. T., Oschman, J. L., & Delany, R. M. (2013). Earthing (Grounding) the human body reduces blood viscosity—a major factor in cardiovascular disease. Journal of Alternative and Complementary Medicine, 19(2), 102–110. https://doi.org/10.1089/acm.2011.0820

Christian, L. (2023). How to Be Your Authentic Self: 7 Powerful Strategies to Be True. *SoulSalt.* https://soulsalt.com/how-to-be-your-authentic-self/#:~:text=Your%20authentic%20self%20is%20who,consistently%20match%20your%20core%20identity.

Cohen, K. (1998). Native American medicine. *PubMed*, 4(6), 45–57. https://pubmed.ncbi.nlm.nih.gov/9810067

Confucius Quotes. (n.d.). BrainyQuote.com. Retrieved December 11, 2023, from BrainyQuote.com Web site: https://www.brainyquote.com/quotes/confucius_104563

Dalai Lama Quotes. (n.d.). BrainyQuote.com. Retrieved December 9, 2023, from BrainyQuote.com Web site: https://www.brainyquote.com/quotes/dalai_lama_166116

Dauvilliers, Y., Siegel, J. M., Lopez, R., Torontali, Z. A., & Peever, J. (2014). Cataplexy—clinical aspects, pathophysiology and management strategy. *Nature Reviews Neurology*, 10(7), 386–395. https://doi.org/10.1038/nrneurol.2014.97

Davis, K. L., Stewart, D., Friedman, J. H., Buchsbaum, M. S., Harvey, P. D., Hof, P. R., Buxbaum, J. D., & Haroutunian, V. (2003).

White matter changes in schizophrenia. *Archives of General Psychiatry, 60*(5), 443. https://doi.org/10.1001/archpsyc.60.5.443

De Bellis, M. D., Keshavan, M. S., Beers, S. R., Hall, J. A., Frustaci, K., Masalehdan, A., Noll, J., & Boring, A. M. (2001). Sex Differences in Brain Maturation during Childhood and Adolescence. *Cerebral Cortex, 11*(6), 552–557. https://doi.org/10.1093/cercor/11.6.552

Denver, J. W. (2004). *The Social Engagement System: Functional Differences in Individuals with Autism.* https://drum.lib.umd.edu/bitstream/1903/1351/1/umi-umd-1486.pdf

Deubner, W. (2022, December 9). FAQ | Aroma Inhaler, Aroma Oils, Bamboo Inhaler. *BrainKick.* https://brain-kick.de/blogs/news/faq-aroma-inhaler-aroma-oils-bamboo-inhaler#:~:text=It%20is%20generally%20safe%20to,once%20or%20twice%20per%20day.

Dimeff, L. A., & Koerner, K. (2007). Dialectical behavior therapy in clinical practice: Applications across disorders and settings. In *Guilford Press eBooks.* https://ci.nii.ac.jp/ncid/BB10311289

Ditlevsen, D. N., & Elklit, A. (2010). The combined effect of gender and age on post traumatic stress disorder: do men and women show differences in the lifespan distribution of the disorder? *Annals of General Psychiatry, 9*(1). https://doi.org/10.1186/1744-859x-9-32

Dorsey, S., McLaughlin, K. A., Kerns, S. E. U., Harrison, J., Lambert, H. K., Briggs, E. C., Cox, J. R., & Amaya-Jackson, L. (2016). Evidence Base Update for Psychosocial Treatments for Children and

Adolescents Exposed to Traumatic Events. *Journal of Clinical Child and Adolescent Psychology, 46*(3), 303–330. https://doi.org/10.1080/15374416.2016.1220309

Epictetus Quotes. (n.d.). BrainyQuote.com. Retrieved December 13, 2023, from BrainyQuote.com Web site: https://www.brainyquote.com/quotes/epictetus_149126

Epictetus Quote: "When someone is properly grounded in life, they shouldn't have to look outside themselves for approval." (n.d.). https://quotefancy.com/quote/2070601/Epictetus-When-someone-is-properly-grounded-in-life-they-shouldn-t-have-to-look-outside

Exclamation, B., & Exclamation, B. (2021, February 1). Healthy diet – Let food be the medicine. | Beyond Exclamation. https://beyondexclamation.com/healthy-diet-let-food-be-the-medicine/

Feenstra, M. G. (2000). Dopamine and noradrenaline release in the prefrontal cortex in relation to unconditioned and conditioned stress and reward. In *Elsevier eBooks* (pp. 133–163). https://doi.org/10.1016/s0079-6123(00)26012-3

Fincham, G. W., Strauss, C., Montero-Marin, J., & Cavanagh, K. (2023). Effect of breathwork on stress and mental health: A meta-analysis of randomised-controlled trials. *Scientific Reports, 13*(1). https://doi.org/10.1038/s41598-022-27247-y

Foa, E. B., & Hearst-Ikeda, D. (1996). Emotional dissociation in response to trauma. In *Springer eBooks* (pp. 207–224). https://doi.org/10.1007/978-1-4899-0310-5_10

Geek, T. (2023, February 10). A neurodivergent review of the safe and sound protocol. *Medium.* https://autietraumageek.medium.com/a-neurodivergent-review-of-the-safe-and-sound-protocol-84e5bc9120bf#:~:text=The%20protocol%20involves%205%20hours,ear%20at%20a%20microsecond%-20pace.

Gershon, M. D. (1999). The enteric nervous system: a second brain. *Hospital Practice*, *34*(7), 31–52. https://doi.org/10.3810/hp.1999.07.153

Gibbons, C. H. (2019). Basics of autonomic nervous system function. In *Handbook of Clinical Neurology* (pp. 407–418). https://doi.org/10.1016/b978-0-444-64032-1.00027-8

Gimpl, G., & Fahrenholz, F. (2001). The oxytocin receptor system: structure, function, and regulation. *Physiological Reviews*, *81*(2), 629–683. https://doi.org/10.1152/physrev.2001.81.2.629

Gitnux. (2023). The Most Surprising Art Therapy Statistics And Trends in 2023 • GITNUX. *GITNUX.* https://blog.gitnux.com/art-therapy-statistics/#:~:text=Studies%20have%20shown%20that%20art,54%25%20and%20provides%20effective%20coping

GoodTherapy Editor Team. (2016, February 23). *Authentic Movement.* https://www.goodtherapy.org/learn-about-therapy/types/authentic-movement

GoodTherapy Editor Team. (2018a, February 28). *The Hakomi Method, Hakomi Experiential Psychotherapy.* https://www.goodtherapy.org/learn-about-therapy/types/hakomi#:~:text=Hakomi%20sessions%20typically%20follow%20a,the%20process%20of%20self%2Dexploration.

GoodTherapy Editor Team. (2018b, March 8). *Somatic Experiencing.* https://www.goodtherapy.org/learn-about-therapy/types/somatic-experiencing#:~:text=Somatic%20Experiencing%20sessions%20involve%20the,or%20a%20shift%20in%20posture.

GoodTherapy Editor Team. (2018c, May 15). *Dance / Movement Therapy.* https://www.goodtherapy.org/learn-about-therapy/types/dance-movement-therapy#:~:text=Research%20has%20demonstrated%20that%20dance,eating%2C%20depression%2C%20and%20anxiety.

Gortner, E. M., Rude, S. S., & Pennebaker, J. W. (2006). Benefits of expressive writing in lowering rumination and depressive symptoms. Behavior Therapy, 37(3), 292–303. https://doi.org/10.1016/j.beth.2006.01.004

Gunter, R. W., & Bodner, G. E. (2008). How eye movements affect unpleasant memories: Support for a working-memory account. *Behaviour Research and Therapy, 46*(8), 913–931. https://doi.org/10.1016/j.brat.2008.04.006

Hakomi Therapy | Therapy Types | Zencare. (n.d.). Hakomi Therapy | Therapy Types | Zencare. https://zencare.co/therapy-type/hakomi

Hamel, J. (2021). *Somatic Art Therapy: Alleviating Pain and Trauma through Art*. Routledge.

Hebb, D. O. (1988). The organization of behavior. In *MIT Press eBooks* (pp. 43–54). http://dl.acm.org/citation.cfm?id=104380

Heck, A. L., & Handa, R. J. (2018). Sex differences in the hypothalamic–pituitary–adrenal axis' response to stress: an important role for gonadal hormones. *Neuropsychopharmacology*, *44*(1), 45–58. https://doi.org/10.1038/s41386-018-0167-9

Heinrichs, M., Baumgartner, T., Kirschbaum, C., & Ehlert, U. (2003). Social support and oxytocin interact to suppress cortisol and subjective responses to psychosocial stress. *Biological Psychiatry*, *54*(12), 1389–1398. https://doi.org/10.1016/s0006-3223(03)00465-7

Hippocrates Quotes. (n.d.). BrainyQuote.com. Retrieved December 10, 2023, from BrainyQuote.com Web site: https://www.brainyquote.com/quotes/hippocrates_481260

Hippocrates Quotes. (n.d.). BrainyQuote.com. Retrieved December 14, 2023, from BrainyQuote.com Web site: https://www.brainyquote.com/quotes/hippocrates_386231

Hollie. (2019, October 10). What Are The Three Stages Of Biofeedback Training? - Monatomic Orme. *Monatomic Orme*. https://monatomic-orme.com/what-are-the-three-stages-of-biofeedback-training/

Holt-Lunstad, J., Smith, T. W., & Layton, J. B. (2010). Social

Relationships and Mortality Risk: A Meta-analytic review. *PLOS Medicine*, *7*(7), e1000316. https://doi.org/10.1371/journal.pmed.1000316

Hoogasian, R., & Lijtmaer, R. M. (2010). Integrating Curanderismo into counselling and psychotherapy. *Counselling Psychology Quarterly*, *23*(3), 297–307. https://doi.org/10.1080/09515070.2010.505752

How a positive mindset boosts your health short course. (n.d.). https://www.calheart.org/video/how-a-positive-mindset-boosts-your-health.html#:~:text=Research%20has%20shown%20that%20positive,recover%20from%20illnesses%20more%20efficiently.

How to increase BDNF: 10 ways to rescue your Brain. (2020, September 17). Strong Coffee Company. https://strongcoffeecompany.com/blogs/strong-words/how-to-increase-bdnf-10-ways-to-rescue-your-brain

How to manipulate brain waves for a Better Mental State | Jefferson Health. (n.d.). https://www.jeffersonhealth.org/your-health/living-well/how-to-manipulate-brain-waves-for-a-better-mental-state#:~:text=Deep%20breathing%20and%20closed%2Deye,release%20of%20the%20neurotransmitter%20serotonin.

How to Prepare for an Optimal Neurofeedback Session. (2023, June 20). https://www.neuropotentialclinics.com/how-to-prepare-for-an-optimal-neurofeedback-session

Ingraham, P. (2023). Bioenergetic Breathing. *www.PainScience.com.* https://www.painscience.com/articles/breathing.php

Innerfire. (2023). New hypothesis suggests Wim Hof Method breathing could accelerate brain waste clearance. *Wim Hof Method.* https://www.wimhofmethod.com/blog/new-hypothesis-suggests-wim-hof-method-breathing-could-accelerate-brain-waste-clearance#:~:text=Researchers%20John%20A.,builds%20up%20in%20the%20brain.

Ishida, K., & Sato, H. (2006). Kampo medicines as alternatives for treatment of migraine: Six case studies. *Complementary Therapies in Clinical Practice.* https://doi.org/10.1016/j.ctcp.2006.07.002

JohnPaulCook. (2019, March 30). *FabulousVagus.png.* Wikimedia Commons. https://upload.wikimedia.org/wikipedia/commons/c/ce/FabulousVagus.png

Johnson, B. (2022, August 19). *Prolonged Exposure Therapy for Post-Traumatic Stress Disorder | Society of Clinical Psychology.* Society of Clinical Psychology | Division 12 of the American Psychological Association. https://div12.org/treatment/prolonged-exposure-therapy-for-post-traumatic-stress-disorder/#:~:text=Essence%20of%20therapy%3A%20Prolonged%20Exposure,were%20safe%20but%20previously%20avoided.

JonesChristiana. (2022, June 13). *Gray and White matter of the cerebrum.png.* Wikimedia Commons. https://upload.wikimedia.org/wikipedia/commons/a/a8/Gray_and_White_

matter_of_the_cerebrum.png

Kajantie, E., & Phillips, D. (2006). The effects of sex and hormonal status on the physiological response to acute psychosocial stress. *Psychoneuroendocrinology*, *31*(2), 151–178. https://doi.org/10.1016/j.psyneuen.2005.07.002

Kang, Y., Komakech, R., Karigar, C. S., & Saqib, A. (2017). Traditional Indian medicine (TIM) and traditional Korean medicine (TKM): aconstitutional-based concept and comparison. *Integrative Medicine Research*, *6*(2), 105–113. https://doi.org/10.1016/j.imr.2016.12.003

Karkou, V., Aithal, S., Zubala, A., & Meekums, B. (2019). Effectiveness of Dance Movement Therapy in the Treatment of Adults With Depression: A Systematic Review With Meta-Analyses. *Frontiers in Psychology*, *10*. https://doi.org/10.3389/fpsyg.2019.00936

Khan Academy. (n.d.). https://www.khanacademy.org/test-prep/mcat/organ-systems/biological-basis-of-behavior-the-nervous-system/v/gray-and-white-matter?modal=1

Kiepe, M., Stöckigt, B., & Keil, T. (2012). Effects of dance therapy and ballroom dances on physical and mental illnesses: A systematic review. *Arts in Psychotherapy*, *39*(5), 404–411. https://doi.org/10.1016/j.aip.2012.06.001

Kolk, V. D., & Bessel, A. (2007). The developmental impact of childhood trauma. In *Cambridge University Press eBooks* (pp. 224–241). https://doi.org/10.1017/cbo9780511500008.016

Lao Tzu Quotes. (n.d.). BrainyQuote.com. Retrieved December 11, 2023, from BrainyQuote.com Web site: https://www.brainyquote. com/quotes/lao_tzu_118184

Lanius, R. A., Rabellino, D., Boyd, J. E., Harricharan, S., Frewen, P. A., & McKinnon, M. C. (2017). The innate alarm system in PTSD: conscious and subconscious processing of threat. Current Opinion in Psychology, 14, 109–115. https://doi.org/10.1016/j. copsyc.2016.11.006

Kropf, J. (2023). 35 Amazing goal setting statistics you should know (2023). *Healthy Happy Impactful*. https:// healthyhappyimpactful.com/goal-setting-statistics/

Kurth, F., Gaser, C., Sánchez, F. J., & Luders, E. (2022). Brain Sex in Transgender Women Is Shifted towards Gender Identity. *Journal of Clinical Medicine*, *11*(6), 1582. https://doi.org/10.3390/ jcm11061582

Lawlor, K. B., & Hornyak, M. J. (2012). Smart Goals: How the application of smart goals can contribute to achievement of student learning outcomes. *Developments in Business Simulation and Experiential Learning*, *29*. https://absel-ojs-ttu.tdl.org/absel/index.php/absel/article/download/90/86

Le, M. (1999). Native American medicine in the treatment of chronic illness: developing an integrated program and evaluating its effectiveness. *PubMed*, *5*(1), 36–44. https:// pubmed.ncbi.nlm.nih.gov/9893314

Lee, J., Sasaki, Y., Arai, I., Go, H., Park, S., Yukawa, K., Nam, Y.,

Ko, S., Motoo, Y., Tsutani, K., & Lee, M. S. (2018). An assessment of the use of complementary and alternative medicine by Korean people using an adapted version of the standardized international questionnaire (I-CAM-QK): a cross-sectional study of an internet survey. *BMC Complementary and Alternative Medicine, 18*(1). https://doi.org/10.1186/s12906-018-2294-6

Levine, P. (2010). *In an Unspoken Voice: How the Body Releases Trauma and Restores Goodness*. https://ci.nii.ac.jp/ncid/BB06082199

Lima, F., Nascimento, E. B., Teixeira, S., Coelho, F. M. S., & Da Paz Oliveira, G. (2019). Thinking outside the box: cataplexy without narcolepsy. *Sleep Medicine, 61*, 118–121. https://doi.org/10.1016/j.sleep.2019.03.006

Little, P., Lewith, G., Webley, F., Evans, M., Beattie, A., Middleton, K., Barnett, J., Ballard, K., Oxford, F., Smith, P., Yardley, L., Hollinghurst, S., & Sharp, D. (2008). Randomised controlled trial of Alexander technique lessons, exercise, and massage (ATEAM) for chronic and recurrent back pain. *BMJ, 337*(aug19 2), a884. https://doi.org/10.1136/bmj.a884

Lord Byron Quotes. (n.d.). BrainyQuote.com. Retrieved December 10, 2023, from BrainyQuote.com Web site: https://www.brainyquote.com/quotes/lord_byron_101256

Luders, E., Sánchez, F. J., Gaser, C., Toga, A. W., Narr, K. L., Hamilton, L. S., & Vilain, E. (2009). Regional gray matter variation in male-to-female transsexualism. *NeuroImage, 46*(4), 904–907. https://doi.org/10.1016/j.neuroimage.2009.03.048

-luffyboy-. (2021, November 4). *Polyvagal theory vagal.png*. https://upload.wikimedia.org/wikipedia/commons/1/17/ Polyvagal_theory_vagal.png

MacPherson, H., Tilbrook, H., Richmond, S., Woodman, J., Ballard, K., Atkin, K., Bland, M., Eldred, J., Essex, H., Hewitt, C., Hopton, A., Keding, A., Lansdown, H., Parrott, S., Torgerson, D., Wenham, A., & Watt, I. (2015). Alexander technique lessons or acupuncture sessions for persons with chronic neck pain. *Annals of Internal Medicine, 163*(9), 653–662. https://doi.org/10.7326/m15-0667

Malhotra, V., Javed, D., Wakode, S., Bharshankar, R., Soni, N., & Porter, P. B. (2022). Study of immediate neurological and autonomic changes during kapalbhati pranayama in yoga practitioners. *Journal of Family Medicine and Primary Care, 11*(2), 720. https://doi.org/10.4103/jfmpc.jfmpc_1662_21

Marcus Aurelius Quotes. (n.d.). BrainyQuote.com. Retrieved December 10, 2023, from BrainyQuote.com Web site: https://www.brainyquote.com/quotes/marcus_aurelius_143090

marilisaraccoglobal. (2018, May 18). *IKEA conducts bullying experiment on plants — the results are shocking*. Global News. Retrieved August 22, 2023, from https://globalnews. ca/news/4217594/bully-a-plant-ikea/#:~:text=In%20a%20 Mythbusters%20experiment%20involving,was%20the%20 death%20metal%20plant

Marlock, G., Weiss, H., Young, C., & Soth, M. (2015). *The Handbook of Body Psychotherapy and Somatic Psychology*. North Atlantic Books.

Mazziotta, J. C., Phelps, M. E., Carson, R. E., & Kuhl, D. E. (1982). Tomographic mapping of human cerebral metabolism: Auditory stimulation. *Neurology, 32*(9), 921. https://doi.org/10.1212/wnl.32.9.921

McCarty, R. (2016a). The Fight-or-Flight response. In *Elsevier eBooks* (pp. 33–37). https://doi.org/10.1016/b978-0-12-800951-2.00004-2

McCarty, R. (2016b). The Fight-or-Flight response. In *Elsevier eBooks* (pp. 33–37). https://doi.org/10.1016/b978-0-12-800951-2.00004-2

Monaco, K. (2022, February 2). Higher oxytocin levels seen in men with hypersexual disorder. *MedPage Today.* https://www.medpagetoday.com/endocrinology/generalendocrinology/96977#:~:text=In%20an%20analysis%20of%20hypersexual,Cyprus%20in%20Nicosia%2C%20and%20colleagues.

Müller, M. S., Vyssotski, A. L., Yamamoto, M., & Yoda, K. (2017). Heart rate variability reveals that a decrease in parasympathetic ('rest-and-digest') activity dominates autonomic stress responses in a free-living seabird. *Comparative Biochemistry & Physiology, 212*, 117–126. https://doi.org/10.1016/j.cbpa.2017.07.007

Najavits, L. M. (2015). Trauma and Substance Abuse: A Clinician's Guide to Treatment. In *A Clinician's Guide to Treatment.* https://doi.org/10.1007/978-3-319-07109-1_16

Napoleon Bonaparte Quotes. (n.d.). BrainyQuote.com. Retrieved

December 13, 2023, from BrainyQuote.com Web site: https://www.brainyquote.com/quotes/napoleon_bonaparte_150189

National Children's Advocacy Center. (n.d.). https://www.nationalcac.org/trauma-focused-cognitive-behavioral-therapy-training/#:~:text=National%20Certification,-Participants%20seeking%20to&text=Participation%20in%20a%20live%20Trauma,per%20month%2C%20for%2012%20months.

Neuhuber, W., & Berthoud, H. (2022). Functional anatomy of the vagus system: How does the polyvagal theory comply? *Biological Psychology*, *174*, 108425. https://doi.org/10.1016/j.biopsycho.2022.108425

Ordaz, S. J., & Luna, B. (2012). Sex differences in physiological reactivity to acute psychosocial stress in adolescence. *Psychoneuroendocrinology*, *37*(8), 1135–1157. https://doi.org/10.1016/j.psyneuen.2012.01.002

Pal, G. K., Agarwal, A., Karthik, S., Pal, P., & Nanda, N. (2014). Slow yogic breathing through right and left nostril influences sympathovagal balance, heart rate variability, and cardiovascular risks in young adults. North American journal of medical sciences, 6(3), 145–151. https://doi.org/10.4103/1947-2714.128477

Park, D. C., & Reuter-Lorenz, P. A. (2009). The adaptive brain: aging and neurocognitive scaffolding. *Annual Review of Psychology*, *60*(1), 173–196. https://doi.org/10.1146/annurev.psych.59.103006.093656

Plutarch Quotes. (n.d.). BrainyQuote.com. Retrieved December 9, 2023, from BrainyQuote.com Web site: https://www.brainyquote.com/quotes/plutarch_161334

Porges, S. W. (2003). The Polyvagal Theory: phylogenetic contributions to social behavior. *Physiology & Behavior*, *79*(3), 503–513. https://doi.org/10.1016/s0031-9384(03)00156-2

Porges, S. W. (2009). The polyvagal theory: New insights into adaptive reactions of the autonomic nervous system. *Cleveland Clinic Journal of Medicine*, *76*(4 suppl 2), S86–S90. https://doi.org/10.3949/ccjm.76.s2.17

Professional, C. C. M. (n.d.). *Biofeedback*. Cleveland Clinic. https://my.clevelandclinic.org/health/treatments/13354-biofeedback#:~:text=During%20a%20biofeedback%20session%2C%20a,make%20adjustments%20without%20the%20equipment.

Psylaris. (2022). Wordt EMDR vergoed door je zorgverzekering? *Psylaris*. https://www.psylaris.com/en/blog/is-emdr-reimbursed-by-your-health-insurance/#:~:text=EMDR%20falls%20under%20the%20basic,referral%20from%20your%20general%20practitioner.

Qigong: What You Need To Know. (n.d.). NCCIH. https://www.nccih.nih.gov/health/qigong-what-you-need-to-know

Ramdinmawii, E., & Mittal, V. K. (2017). The effect of music on the human mind: A study using brainwaves and binaural beats. *2017 2nd International Conference on Telecommunication and*

Networks (TEL-NET). https://doi.org/10.1109/tel-net.2017.8343514

Recurrent laryngeal nerve.svg. (2014, February 5). Wikimedia Commons. https://upload.wikimedia.org/wikipedia/commons/6/64/Recurrent_laryngeal_nerve.svg

Resick, P. A., Monson, C. M., & Chard, K. M. (2016). *Cognitive Processing Therapy for PTSD: A Comprehensive Manual.*

Rice, A. (2022, January 4). *Trauma-Informed Yoga: A Guide.* Psych Central. https://psychcentral.com/health/what-is-trauma-informed-yoga

Rothschild, B. (2000). *The body remembers: The psychophysiology of trauma and trauma treatment.* https://psycnet.apa.org/record/2006-04919-000

Roy, A., Sarchiapone, M., & Carli, V. (2007). Low resilience in suicide attempters. *Archives of Suicide Research, 11*(3), 265–269. https://doi.org/10.1080/13811110701403916

Sapra, R. (2023). Reflecting and integrating the inner child during challenging times. In *Routledge eBooks* (pp. 20–25). https://doi.org/10.4324/9781003255895-3

Scantlebury, D. C., & Prasad, A. (2014). Diagnosis of takotsubo cardiomyopathy. *Circulation Journal, 78*(9), 2129–2139. https://doi.org/10.1253/circj.cj-14-0859

Seeking safety. (n.d.). SAMHSA. https://www.samhsa.gov/

resource/dbhis/seeking-safety

Seneca the Younger. (n.d.). AZQuotes.com. Retrieved December 15, 2023, from AZQuotes.com Web site: https://www.azquotes.com/quote/567798

SIDDHA SOLUTION FOR CHRONIC DISEASES. (n.d.). Sri Raghavendra Hospital - Siddha, Ayurveda, Varma. https://raghavendraspinecare.com/siddha-solution-for-chronic-diseases/

Sinha, P. K. (n.d.). The interconnected worlds of quantum physics and spirituality. www.linkedin.com. https://www.linkedin.com/pulse/interconnected-worlds-quantum-physics-spirituality-pritam-kumar-sinha#:~:text=Quantum%20entanglement%20challenges%20our%20conventional,concept%20of%20oneness%20or%20unity.

Spinhoven, P., Penninx, B. W. J. H., Van Hemert, A. M., De Rooij, M., & Elzinga, B. M. (2014). Comorbidity of PTSD in anxiety and depressive disorders: Prevalence and shared risk factors. Child Abuse & Neglect, 38(8), 1320–1330. https://doi.org/10.1016/j.chiabu.2014.01.017

Stall, P., & Teixeira, M. J. (2014). Fibromyalgia syndrome treated with the structural integration Rolfing®method. Revista DOR, 15(4). https://doi.org/10.5935/1806-0013.20140053

Stress system malfunction could lead to serious, life threatening disease. (2002, September 9). https://www.nichd.nih.gov/. https://www.nichd.nih.gov/newsroom/releases/stress

Sun, L., Peräkylä, J., Holm, K., Haapasalo, J., Lehtimäki, K., Ogawa, K. H., Peltola, J., & Hartikainen, K. M. (2017). Vagus nerve stimulation improves working memory performance. *Journal of Clinical and Experimental Neuropsychology*, *39*(10), 954–964. https://doi.org/10.1080/13803395.2017.1285869

Tarr, B., Launay, J., Cohen, E., & Dunbar, R. (2015). Synchrony and exertion during dance independently raise pain threshold and encourage social bonding. *Biology Letters*, *11*(10), 20150767. https://doi.org/10.1098/rsbl.2015.0767

The developing brain on JSTOR. (n.d.). www.jstor.org. https://doi.org/10.2307/24939213

The Editors of Encyclopaedia Britannica. (2023, July 14). *Unani medicine | Ancient Healing Practices & Benefits*. Encyclopedia Britannica. https://www.britannica.com/science/Unani-medicine

The persistence of traditional medicine in the modern world. (2023, March 14). Cultural Survival. https://www.culturalsurvival.org/publications/cultural-survival-quarterly/persistence-traditional-medicine-modern-world#:~:text=Contrary%20to%20those%20beliefs%2C%20however,or%20loss%20of%20self%2Desteem.

Theodore Roosevelt Quotes. (n.d.). BrainyQuote.com. Retrieved December 10, 2023, from BrainyQuote.com Web site: https://www.brainyquote.com/quotes/theodore_roosevelt_100965

Thulin, K., & Thulin, K. (2020). Signs you've been triggered:

examples of trauma symptoms. *Catalyst Center*. https://catalystcenterllc.com/signs-youve-been-triggered-examples-of-trauma-symptoms/

Tnn. (2019). The science behind healing crystals explained! *The Times of India*. https://timesofindia.indiatimes.com/life-style/health-fitness/home-remedies/the-science-behind-healing-crystals-explained/articleshow/70482968.cms

Toumpanakis, A., Turnbull, T., & Alba-Barba, I. (2018). Effectiveness of plant-based diets in promoting well-being in the management of type 2 diabetes: a systematic review. BMJ Open Diabetes Research & Care, 6(1), e000534. https://doi.org/10.1136/bmjdrc-2018-000534

Travis, F. (2001). Autonomic and EEG patterns distinguish transcending from other experiences during Transcendental Meditation practice. *International Journal of Psychophysiology*, *42*(1), 1–9. https://doi.org/10.1016/s0167-8760(01)00143-x

Travis, F. (2012). *Your Brain Is a River, Not a Rock* (3rd ed.).

Van Den Hout, M. A., & Engelhard, I. M. (2012). How does EMDR work? *Journal of Experimental Psychopathology*, *3*(5), 724–738. https://doi.org/10.5127/jep.028212

View of A Traumatic Event | Bioenergetic Analysis. (n.d.). https://bioenergetic-analysis.com/article/view/0743-4804-2021-31-111/html

Weber, C., Thayer, J. F., Rudat, M., Wirtz, P. H., Zimmermann-

Viehoff, F., Thomas, A., Perschel, F. H., Arck, P. C., & Deter, H. (2010). Low vagal tone is associated with impaired post stress recovery of cardiovascular, endocrine, and immune markers. *European Journal of Applied Physiology, 109*(2), 201–211. https://doi.org/10.1007/s00421-009-1341-x

West, J. L., Liang, B., & Spinazzola, J. (2017). Trauma sensitive yoga as a complementary treatment for posttraumatic stress disorder: A qualitative descriptive analysis. *International Journal of Stress Management, 24*(2), 173–195. https://doi.org/10.1037/str0000040

What are arts and creative therapies? (n.d.). Mind. https://www.mind.org.uk/information-support/drugs-and-treatments/talking-therapy-and-counselling/arts-and-creative-therapies/

What to Expect During a Biofeedback Session. (n.d.). PainScale. https://www.painscale.com/article/what-to-expect-during-a-biofeedback-session

Why Breathwork Is So Powerful And How To Do It. (2021, March 27). https://www.thewayofmeditation.com.au/why-breathwork-is-so-powerful-and-how-to-do-it#:~:text=Neuroscientists%20have%20made%20a%20direct,being%20in%20%E2%80%9Cthe%20zone%E2%80%9D.&text=Breathwork%20is%20an%20effective%20way,patterns%2C%20stress%20and%20depression%20levels.

William James Quotes. (n.d.). BrainyQuote.com. Retrieved

December 11, 2023, from BrainyQuote.com Web site: https://www.brainyquote.com/quotes/william_james_157186

William James Quotes. (n.d.). BrainyQuote.com. Retrieved December 9, 2023, from BrainyQuote.com Web site: https://www.brainyquote.com/quotes/william_james_385478

William Shakespeare Quotes. (n.d.). BrainyQuote.com. Retrieved December 9, 2023, from BrainyQuote.com Web site: https://www.brainyquote.com/quotes/william_shakespeare_101008

Williamson, A. (2023). *Somatic Movement Dance Therapy: The Healing Art of Self-Regulation and Co-Regulation.* Intellect (UK).

Wisdom, T. (2023, March 21). *How Bioenergetics Therapy Works, Online Therapist Training, Laurie Ure - Therapy Wisdom.* Therapy Wisdom. https://therapywisdom.com/2023/03/21/bioenergetics-therapy-training-laurie-ure/

Wiwatwongwana, D., Vichitvejpaisal, P., Thaikruea, L., Klaphajone, J., Tantong, A., & Wiwatwongwana, A. (2016). The effect of music with and without binaural beat audio on operative anxiety in patients undergoing cataract surgery: a randomized controlled trial. *Eye, 30*(11), 1407–1414. https://doi.org/10.1038/eye.2016.160

Xie, L., Kang, H., Xu, Q., Chen, M., Liao, Y., Thiyagarajan, M., O'Donnell, J., Christensen, D. J., Nicholson, C., Iliff, J.

J., Takano, T., & Deane, R. (2013). Sleep Drives Metabolite Clearance from the Adult Brain. *Science*, *342*(6156), 373–377. https://doi.org/10.1126/science.1241224

Yadav, R. K., Magan, D., Mehta, N., Sharma, R., & Mahapatra, S. C. (2012). Efficacy of a Short-Term Yoga-Based Lifestyle intervention in reducing stress and inflammation: Preliminary results. *Journal of Alternative and Complementary Medicine*, *18*(7), 662–667. https://doi.org/10.1089/acm.2011.0265

Yehuda, R., Giller, E. L., Southwick, S. M., Lowy, M. T., & Mason, J. (1991). Hypothalamic-pituitary-adrenal dysfunction in posttraumatic stress disorder. *Biological Psychiatry*, *30*(10), 1031–1048. https://doi.org/10.1016/0006-3223(91)90123-4

Zaccaro, A., Piarulli, A., Laurino, M., Garbella, E., Menicucci, D., Neri, B., & Gemignani, A. (2018). How Breath-Control Can Change Your Life: A systematic review on Psycho-Physiological correlates of slow breathing. *Frontiers in Human Neuroscience*, *12*. https://doi.org/10.3389/fnhum.2018.00353

Zak, P. J., Stanton, A. A., & Ahmadi, S. (2007). Oxytocin increases generosity in humans. *PLOS ONE*, *2*(11), e1128. https://doi.org/10.1371/journal.pone.0001128

Zhang, Y. H., & Rose, K. (2001). *A brief history of Qi.* https://philpapers.org/rec/ZHAABH

Made in United States
Troutdale, OR
04/25/2024

19451024R00189